佳　肴　菜　Chinese　谱　系　列
Genuine

家禽美食
Poultry Cuisine

Poultry Cuisine
家禽美食

家禽是我们日常膳食中最常用的材料，而家禽中又以鸡最受欢迎。尤其是广东人简直是无鸡不欢。请客宴会，鸡经常是主角。没有鸡的筵席就好像没有了灵魂。

广东人请客用的鸡通常是全鸡才算隆重。像白切鸡、梅子烧鸡、玫瑰油鸡等都是大名鼎鼎的筵席菜式。其实鸡的价钱并不比其他肉类贵，相反地鸡比猪肉、牛肉更便宜。但猪、牛肉反而不能登大雅之堂。筵席上绝少见到牛肉、猪肉的踪迹。究其因是鸡的肉质比其他肉类嫩滑，而且可以和许多瓜果蔬菜同炒，滋味极佳。鸡肉除了美味嫩滑之

外，营养价值也极高，是老幼咸宜的营养食品。

　　鸡肉的肉质组织柔软，脂肪分布平均，胆固醇含量很低，含丰富之维他命及蛋白质，而且易于消化，最适宜作病人及老人家的补品。

　　由于鸡肉是对人体最滋养的肉类，所以此书大部分菜肴都是环绕着鸡作研究。其中包括有用鸡胸肉及鸡柳作材料的西芹鸡柳、茄汁鸡丁、子萝鸡片等菜式，因为鸡柳及胸肉嫩滑而不含脂肪宜于作小炒。也有宜于宴客的全鸡菜式如金华肉树鸡、玫瑰油鸡；更有儿童最爱的鸡翼制作如盐水浸鸡翼、盐焗鸡翼、香葱焗鸡翼等。

THE AUTHOR

Cecilia Jennie Au-Yang graduated in home economics from Grantham Teacher Training College, Hong Kong, in 1956. Over the years,she studied cooking in her spare time with famous Hong Kong chefs.

In 1971, she founded Chopsticks Cooking Centre to provide the best facilities for teaching Chinese home cooking.

Since 1974, she has taught professional cookery training courses for people interested in working in catering.The courses enable students to learn cooking while working as trainees and gaining work experience. Many graduates from these courses have successfully found employment in the food and catering industries overseas.

Cecilia set up Chopsticks Publications Limited in 1975 to publish her own recipes-the "Chopsticks Recipes" series with one colour photograph per dish and English and Chinese text.

In 1984, Chopsticks Publications Limited entered the UK market when Cecilia co-published a 240-page hardcover Chinese cookery book "The Best of Chinese Cooking" with Hamlyn Publishing,England. The following year the book was translated into Dutch.

In 1989,She wrote a series of five popular pocket-sized cookery books for the Japanese Publisher, Tokuma Shoten.

To date she has written and published a total of 22 cookery books.

Cecilia has also been writing cookery columns for various well-known Hong Kong magazines and newspapers,and has acted as a consultant to several food manufacturers, testing and writing new recipes as well as training sales representatives in using their own products.

Cecilia Au-Yang's cookery books are used worldwide by housewives, gourmets and professional chefs.

作者简介

欧阳纫溆女士1956年毕业于香港葛量洪教育学院家政系。在其教学生涯中，欧阳女士利用空闲时间努力于研究厨艺。

1971年欧阳女士开始设帐授徒，专门教授家庭小菜。

1974年首创半工读烹饪培训班，训练欲投身饮食业之人士。是项课程对热爱烹饪人士提供一个良好的学习机会。历年来之毕业生移居外地经营饮食业而扬威海外者甚众。

1975年欧阳女士成立嘉馔出版有限公司，首创中英对照，每菜一图之彩色食谱《美点佳肴》书集。

1984年《美点佳肴》被英国大出版社 HAMLYN PUBLISHING 购买版权，辑成一本 240 页精装食谱："THE BEST OF CHINESE COOKING"。翌年更被翻译为荷兰文。

1989年《美点佳肴》进入日本市场，为日本大出版社德间文库编成五本袋装食谱。

至今欧阳女士已写作及出版 26 本食谱。

多年来，欧阳女士除教授烹饪外，并专心致力为食品公司试验新产品、设计新食谱及培训食品推广人士。

欧阳纫溆女士之食谱深受世界各地的主妇、美食家及职业厨师所欢迎及采用。

Content

Miscellaneous 杂类

烧焗珍肝
BAKED CHICKEN LIVERS

材料：

鸡肝 360 克　　　蒜头 2 粒
姜 15 克　　　　　蜜糖 3 汤匙
葱头 2 粒　　　　　麻油 1 茶匙涂面

配料：

老抽 2 汤匙　　　糖 2 汤匙
生抽 2 汤匙　　　玫瑰露 1 汤匙
红粉水 1 汤匙

制法：

◆ 鸡肝洗净以毛巾吸干水份。
◆ 姜、葱、蒜头全切开，放入搅拌器中打烂成泥，以胶刮刮出放在一个深碟上。
◆ 腌料加在碟中与姜、葱、蒜泥一同搅拌至糖溶。即将鸡肝放入反覆沾满腌料。置一旁腌 1 小时。
◆ 焗炉预开至 200℃。
◆ 长方焗盆一个内铺锡纸，上面架一涂油铁丝网或不锈钢架，将鸡肝排放铁网上。放入焗炉中焗 10 分钟。取出淋以蜜糖。反转重放炉内再焗 10 分钟。熄去炉火将鸡肝取出涂上麻油，切厚件上碟。

Ingredients:

360g chicken livers
15g ginger
2 shallots

2 garlic cloves
3 tbsp honey
1 tsp sesame oil

Marinade:

2 tbsp dark soy
2 tbsp light soy
l tbsp red food colouring (optional)

2 tbsp sugar
1 tbsp rose wine or cooking sherry

Method:

◆ Wash and towel dry the chicken livers.
◆ Chop the ginger, shallots and garlic coarsely, then blend into a puree with a food processor. Scrape the puree on to a saucer.
◆ Mix the marinade with the puree and stir until the sugar dissolves. Coat the livers thoroughly with the mixed marinade. Set aside to infuse for an hour.
◆ Preheat the oven to 200℃.
◆ Line an oblong baking tray with aluminium foil and top it with a greased rack.
◆ Arrange the livers on the rack and place them in the middle shelf of the oven then bake for 10 minutes. Remove and coat with the honey. Turn the livers and bake in the oven for a further 10 minutes. Turn off the heat and remove the livers on to a chopping board. Brush with sesame oil then slice into thick pieces and arrange on a platter. Serve hot or cold.

芫荽鸡翼

BAKED CHICKEN WINGS WITH PARSLEY

材料:

鸡翼 500 克约 4 只　　　姜 2 片
葱头 30 克　　　　　　　芫荽 60 克
蒜头 15 克　　　　　　　炸油 $1/2$ 锅
　　　　　　　　　　　　另麻油 1 汤匙涂面

腌料:

姜汁 1 汤匙　　　　　　　鸡粉 $1/2$ 茶匙
酒 1 汤匙　　　　　　　　胡椒粉 $1/8$ 茶匙
生抽 $2^1/2$ 汤匙　　　　　麻油 1 茶匙
糖 1 汤匙

制法:

◆ 鸡翼洗净抹干，放在深碟内候用。
◆ 葱、蒜头及姜片剁茸。芫荽洗净亦剁茸。
◆ 将全部茸放在小碗内，加入调味料拌至糖溶。试妥味倒在鸡翼上捞匀腌约 4 小时。
◆ 烧红锅，倒入油半锅煮至沸时。将鸡翼滑下炸片刻，捞起隔去余油。
◆ 将鸡翼放在已涂油之架上，盛在焗盘中。置已预热之 220℃ 焗炉内焗 5 分钟，取出涂上麻油再焗 5 分钟即成。

Ingredients:

4 chicken wings,　　　　60g parsley
about 500g　　　　　　　$1/2$ wok oil for deep
30g shallots　　　　　　　frying
15g garlic　　　　　　　　1 extra tbsp sesame oil
2 slices ginger　　　　　for brushing

Marinade:

1 tbsp ginger juice　　　$1/2$ tsp chicken powder
1 tbsp wine　　　　　　　$1/8$ tsp pepper
$2^1/2$ tbsp Light soy　　　1 tsp sesame oil
1 tbsp sugar

Method :

◆ Wash, dry and place the chicken wings on a platter.
◆ Mince the shallots, garlic and ginger. Wash and mince the parsley.
◆ Put all the minced ingredients into a small bowl then add the marinade and stir until the sugar dissolves. Adjust the seasoning according to taste and pour over the chicken wings to mix thoroughly. Set aside for 4 hours.
◆ Heat a wok and bring the oil to the boil. Slide in the wings to deep fry for 2 to 3 minutes until golden brown. Remove and drain.
◆ Put the chicken wings on to a greased rack over a baking tray and place in a preheated oven of 220℃ to bake for 5 minutes. Remove and brush with the sesame oil. Bake for a further 5 minutes. Dish and serve hot or cold.

金华玉树鸡

BONELESS CHICKEN WITH HAM

材料:

光鸡1只, 重1500克　　火腿180克
粗盐1汤匙　　　　　　沸水3杯
姜3片　　　　　　　　菜软300克
葱3条　　　　　　　　油2汤匙
八角2粒　　　　　　　葱头2粒

调味:

盐2茶匙　　　　　　　糖 $1/2$ 茶匙
酒2茶匙　　　　　　　胡椒粉 $1/8$ 茶匙
上汤 $2/3$ 杯　　　　　生粉水1汤匙
生抽1茶匙　　　　　　麻油1茶匙

制法:

◆ 光鸡用粗盐擦净鸡皮, 冲洗干净, 以毛巾吸
　干水份。

◆ 鸡皮用盐及酒各1茶匙涂匀。鸡肚以另一半
　盐及酒、姜片、葱及八角塞入摇匀。放蒸笼
　内猛火蒸20分钟。停火取出晾凉去骨切成
　骨牌片。

◆ 火腿放入沸水中飞水, 过冷河隔干水份。沸
　水留起候用。火腿亦切成骨牌片, 然后将鸡
　与火腿梅花间竹地排在长碟上。

◆ 菜软用留下沸水飞水, 隔去水份, 排在碟
　边。

◆ 烧红锅加油煮沸爆香葱头后弃去, 倾下上汤
　加调味料试妥味, 以生粉水流入和成稀芡,
　淋上鸡肉上即可上桌。

Ingredients:

1 chicken, about 1500g　　3 cups boiling water
1 tbsp coarse salt　　　　300g green vegetables
3 slices ginger　　　　　2 tbsp oil
3 chives　　　　　　　　2 shallots
2 star anises
180g Virginia
ham

Seasoning:

2 tsp salt　　　　　　　 $1/2$ tsp sugar
2 tsp sherry　　　　　　 $1/8$ tsp pepper
$2/3$ cup stock　　　　　1 tbsp cornflour mix
1 tsp light soy　　　　　1 tsp sesame oil

Method:

◆ Clean the chicken skin by rubbing with the salt. Refresh and dry with a towel.

◆ Rub 1 tsp each of the salt and sherry over the chicken skin. Place another tsp of salt and sherry, the ginger, chives and star anises inside the chicken. Steam over high heat for 20 minutes then remove and leave to cool. Debone and cut the chicken into bite-sized pieces.

◆ Blanch the ham in the boiling water. Refresh and drain. Keep the water for later use. Cut the ham into similar size as the chicken. Arrange the ham and chicken slices alternatively on an oval platter.

◆ Blanch the green vegetables in the above boiling water. Drain and arrange round the chicken and ham.

◆ Heat the oil in a hot wok to saute the shallots then discard. Pour in the stock and season to taste. Thicken the sauce with the cornflour mix. Pour evenly over the dish and serve hot.

冬菇汽锅鸡

CHICKEN AND MUSHROOM IN YUNNAN POT

材料：

冬菇60克	鸡1只约1000克
温水 2杯	水8杯
盐¹/₂茶匙	姜2片
糖¹/₂茶匙	油1汤匙

调味：

盐1¹/₂茶匙	糖¹/₂茶匙

制法：

◆ 冬菇洗净浸温水中至软身，剪去蒂，以盐、糖、油捞匀腌片刻。

◆ 鸡洗净抹干。鸡肉与皮用刀分离。慢慢撕去鸡皮。弃去或留作别用。

◆ 取去鸡油及内脏，将鸡身分成2份。置沸水内飞水约1分钟。取出放水龙头下冲洗干净。

◆ 汽锅放水（包括冬菇水），加姜片及鸡，盖上锅盖，放置沸水锅上以中火炖2小时。倒入冬菇续炖30分钟。

◆ 试妥味即可上桌。

Ingredients:

60g Chinese mushrooms	1 tbsp oil
	1 chicken, about 1000g
2 cups warm water	8 cups water
¹/₂ tsp salt	2 slices ginger
¹/₂ tsp sugar	

Seasoning:

1¹/₂ tsp salt	¹/₂ tsp sugar

Method:

◆ Wash and soak the mushrooms in the warm water until soft. Cut off the stems and marinate with the salt, sugar and oil.

◆ Wash the chicken, slash a cut in the centre front or back to separate the skin from the body. Gently pull the skin away by tearing the membrane between the skin and the flesh. Discard or keep the skin for other usage.

◆ Remove all the fat and giblet from the carcass and cut the skinless chicken into halves. Blanch in some boiling water for a minute. Refresh and drain.

◆ Pour the water (including mushroom stock) into a Yunnan Pot; add the ginger and chicken. Put the lid on and place the casserole over a pot of boiling water. Steam for 2 hours over moderate heat.

◆ Add the mushrooms and continue to steam for another 30 minutes. Season to taste and serve hot in the Yunnan Pot.

2

1

3

4

5

砂锅鸡鲍翅
CHICKEN AND SHARK'S FIN CASSEROLE

材料：

水发鲍翅 1000 克	上鸡 1 只约 1500 克
沸水 1/2 锅	发好鲍鱼 2 只
姜 4 片	熟冬菇 1 只
葱 4 棵	火腿 30 克
酒 1 汤匙	冬笋 125 克
上汤 6 杯	清水 2 杯

调味：

盐 2 茶匙	胡椒粉 1/4 茶匙

制法：

◆ 将鲍翅放入沸水中焓 1/2 小时，取出洗净。沸水留后用，姜、葱拍扁。

◆ 烧红锅，潜酒加姜、葱。倒入上汤 2 杯，将鲍翅放入煨 20 分钟。倒出隔去水份，弃去姜葱。

◆ 上鸡洗净除去头颈及爪在背部剖开，放沸水中飞水后再洗干净。

◆ 鲍鱼片成薄片。冬菇开边。火腿、冬笋放清水中煮 1 分钟切长条候用。

◆ 砂锅洗净，将鸡平放在下，鲍鱼铺在上面，再铺上鲍翅排好，上汤倒至盖过翅面。文火熬 3 小时，揭盖加调味品试妥味后，将冬菇、火腿、笋片排在翅面。盖上锅盖，再熬 1 小时，即可食用。

Ingredients:

1000g presoaked shark's fin	2 precooked abalones
	1 large cooked Chinese mushroom
1/2 wok boiling water	30g ham
4 slices ginger	125g bamboo shoots
4 spring onions	
1 tbsp wine	2 cups water
6 cups stock	
1 chicken, about 1500g	

Seasoning:

2 tsp salt	1/4 tsp pepper

Method:

◆ Put the shark's fin in the boiling water to simmer for 30 minutes. Remove and wash thoroughly. Retain the boiling water. Mash the ginger and spring onions.

◆ Heat a saucepan until hot, sizzle the wine to saute the ginger and spring onions. Pour in 2 cups of the stock and shark's fin to bring to the boil then simmer for 20 minutes. Drain and discard the stock, ginger and spring onions.

◆ Clean and chop the head, neck and claws off the chicken. Slash the chicken at the back to flatten. Blanch in the above boiling water and refresh.

◆ Slice the abalones and halve the mushroom. Put the ham and bamboo shoots in the water to bring to boil then blanch for a minute. Refresh, drain and slice into oblong pieces.

◆ Prepare a big casserole and lay the chicken with the skin facing down. Put in a layer of the sliced abalone and the shark's fin then pour in the stock just enough to cover all the ingredients. Simmer over low heat for 3 hours. Remove the lid and season to taste. Arrange the mushroom, ham and the bamboo shoots on the shark's fin and continue to simmer for another hour. Remove and serve hot.

鸡肉青瓜串

CHICKEN AND VEGETABLE KEBABS

材料:

鸡肉 250 克 　　　　青瓜 125 克
姜 2 片 　　　　　　番茄或红萝卜 125 克
蒜头 2 粒 　　　　　油 3 汤匙扫面
葱头 2 粒

腌料:

姜汁 1 茶匙 　　　　生抽 1 汤匙
酒 1 茶匙 　　　　　胡椒粉 1/2 茶匙
茄汁 1 汤匙 　　　　水 1/4 杯
喼汁 1 汤匙 　　　　生粉 1 茶匙
糖 1 茶匙 　　　　　麻油 1/2 汤匙（后下）

特别器具:

竹签或钢针 2 打

制法:

◆ 鸡肉洗净抹干切成约 1.25 公分丁方粒。
◆ 姜、蒜头、葱头去衣剁茸放在大碗中，与上述腌料（除麻油）一同和匀。加入鸡粒捞匀腌约 30 分钟，将麻油拌入再腌 30 分钟。
◆ 青瓜洗净去籽切丁方粒。番茄亦洗净切同样大小粒候用。
◆ 竹签或钢针涂油穿上一粒鸡肉，一粒青瓜；第二粒鸡肉，一粒番茄；再穿最后一粒鸡肉，放在已涂油之架上盛在焗盘中，置已预热 200℃，焗炉内焗 5 分钟；取出涂油放回炉中再焗 5 分钟至金黄色即成。共得串烧鸡约 2 打。
注: 如用红萝卜可先飞水而后切粒。

Ingredients:

250g chicken fillet　　　2 shallots
2 slices ginger　　　　125g cucumber
2 garlic cloves　　　　125g tomatoes
　　　　　　　　　　　3 tbsp oil for brushing

Marinade:

1 tsp ginger juice　　　1 tbsp light soy
1 tsp wine　　　　　　1/2 tsp pepper
1 tbsp tomato ketchup　1/4 cup water
1 tbsp Worcestershire sauce　　1 tsp cornflour
1 tsp sugar　　　　　　1/2 tbsp sesame oil, to be added last

Special Utensils:

24 skewers

Method:

◆ Wash, dry and dice the chicken into 1.25 cm cubes.
◆ Mince the ginger, garlic and shallots. Put into a mixing bowl and stir well with the above marinade (except the sesame oil). Immerse the chicken to stand for 30 minutes then blend in the sesame oil to marinate for a further 30 minutes.
◆ Wash, deseed and dice the cucumber. Wash and dice the tomatoes into similar size to the cucumber.
◆ Skewer a piece each of chicken, cucumber and tomato alternately. Put on a greased rack in a baking tray and bake for 5 minutes in a preheated 200℃ oven. Remove and brush with the oil. Return into the oven to bake for another 5 minutes until golden brown. Serve hot.

鸡粥

CHICKEN CONGEE

材料：

鸡肉 500 克	腐皮 2 张
米 1/2 杯	水 12 杯
盐 1 茶匙	姜丝 1 汤匙
油 1 汤匙	芫荽 1 茶匙
白果 10 粒	

腌料：

姜汁 1 茶匙	胡椒粉 1/8 茶匙
酒 1 茶匙	生粉 1 汤匙
生抽 1 茶匙	麻油 1 茶匙
糖 1/2 茶匙	

调味：

盐 1 1/2 茶匙	胡椒粉 1/4 茶匙

制法：

◆ 鸡去皮洗净抹干切件，以和匀腌料腌 20 分钟候用。

◆ 米洗净以盐、油捞匀。白果去壳去衣、腐皮洗净撕碎。

◆ 将水注入压力煲内，加入米、白果及腐皮，以大火煮沸后转用文火煮 20 分钟。揭盖拌入鸡件续煮 5 分钟。调妥味，洒下姜丝、芫荽热食。

Ingredients:

500g chicken meat	10 gingko nuts
	2 bean curd sheets
1/2 cup rice	12 cups water
1 tsp salt	1 tbsp shredded ginger
1 tbsp oil	1 tbsp parsley

Marinade:

1 tsp ginger juice	1/8 tsp pepper
1 tsp wine	1 tbsp cornflour
1 tsp light soy	1 tsp sesame oil
1/2 tsp sugar	

Seasoning:

1 1/2 tsp salt	1/4 tsp pepper

Method:

◆ Cut the chicken into large pieces and immerse in the marinade for 20 minutes.

◆ Rinse the rice and mix with the salt and oil. Shell and peel the gingko nuts. Wash and tear the bean curd sheets into small pieces.

◆ Pour the water, rice, gingko nuts and bean curd sheets into the pressure cooker and bring to the boil. Lower the heat; simmer for 20 minutes. Stir in the chicken and cook for another 5 minutes. Season to taste, then ladle into soup bowls and serve hot, with the ginger and parsley sprinkled on top.

杂菜鸡心

CHICKEN HEARTS WITH MIXED VEGETABLES

材料：

鸡心 20 个
草菇 60 克
红萝卜 60 克
马蹄 60 克

青豆 60 克
油 1 汤匙
姜 2 片
葱头、蒜头各 2 粒

腌料：

姜汁 1 汤匙
酒 1 汤匙

生粉 1/2 汤匙

调味：

盐 1/2 茶匙
酒 1 茶匙
上汤 1/2 杯
生抽 1 茶匙

蚝油 1 茶匙
糖 1 茶匙
胡椒粉 1/4 茶匙

芡料：

生粉水 2 茶匙
老抽 1/4 茶匙

麻油 1 茶匙

制法：

◆ 鸡心洗净，在尖端以刀剥两个十字使成八瓣。每刀只剥约四分之三。再洗净抹干放碗中加腌料拌匀腌 1 小时。泡油候用。

◆ 草菇削去蒂在尖端剥十字。红萝卜切花片，马蹄去皮洗净切片，青豆洗净。全部材料置沸水中飞水后冲冻。姜切指甲片。葱、蒜头亦切片。

◆ 阔口碗 1 只将已开八瓣之鸡心排放入内，花瓣向底。

◆ 烧红锅加油煮沸，放入姜、葱、蒜片及盐爆香。倾下全部配料同炒片刻，灒酒加上汤及调味和匀，铲起淋在鸡心上。转置猛火蒸笼内蒸 10 分钟，取出将汁倒起，其余材料则反扣在深碟内。

◆ 汤汁放小锅内煮沸，慢慢流下芡料拌匀淋在心花上即成。

Ingredients:

20 pieces chicken heart
60g straw mushrooms
60g carrots
60g water chestnuts

60g sweet peas
1 tbsp oil
2 slices ginger
2 shallots
2 garlic cloves

Marinade:

1 tbsp ginger juice
1 tbsp wine

$^1/_2$ tbsp cornflour

Seasoning:

$^1/_2$ tsp salt
1 tsp wine
$^1/_2$ cup stock
1 tsp light soy

1 tsp oyster sauce
1 tsp sugar
$^1/_2$ tsp pepper

Gravy Mix:

2 tsp cornflour mix
$^1/_2$ tsp dark soy

1 tsp sesame oil

Method:

◆ Wash the chicken hearts and slash two crosses on each tip. The slashes must be only $^3/_4$ of the thickness of the hearts. Clean again, towel dry and immerse in the mixed marinade for l hour then parboil and drain.

◆ Trim and cut a cross on the top of each straw mushroom. Carve and slice the carrots. Peel, clean and slice the water chestnuts. Wash the sweet peas and blanch all the ingredients in boiling water then refresh. Cut the ginger into fingernail-sized pieces. Slice the shallots and garlic.

◆ Place the hearts in a bowl with the slashed tips faced down.

◆ Heat a wok with 2 tbsp oil to saute the ginger, shallots, garlic and salt. Put in all the ingredients and fry for a while. Sizzle the wine, add the stock and seasoning and mix well. Scoop over the hearts and place in a steamer to cook for 10 minutes over high heat. Remove and pour the juice into a container. Invert the bowl of hearts and vegetables on to a plate.

◆ Bring the juice to boil in a saucepan and trickle in the gravy mix to thicken it. Mask over the hearts and serve hot.

麻辣鸡件
CHICKEN IN HOT SESAME PASTE

材料:

鸡肉 300 克	生粉 1 杯
麻酱 1 汤匙	油 4 杯
芥酱 1 汤匙	番荽 1 棵
蛋 1 只打烂	

调味:

姜汁 2 茶匙	盐 $1/4$ 茶匙
酒 1 茶匙	糖 1 茶匙
生抽 1 茶匙	胡椒粉 $1/8$ 茶匙
生粉 1 茶匙	

制法:

◆ 鸡肉切片加麻酱、芥酱及全部调味料捞匀腌 30 分钟。

◆ 鸡蛋放入鸡件中拌匀，隔去腌料，再上干生粉。

◆ 烧红锅注入油煮沸，将鸡件投入炸约 4 分钟至金黄色。盛起晾凉。

◆ 晾凉后再炸 1 分钟，隔去余油，切成小件，排放在碟上。以红萝卜花及番荽装饰。喼汁、淮盐跟上。

Ingredients:

300g boneless chicken	1 beaten egg
	1 cup cornflour
1 tbsp sesame paste	4 cups oil
1 tbsp hot mustard	1 parsley sprig

Seasoning:

2 tap ginger juice	$1/4$ tsp salt
1 tsp sherry	1 tsp sugar
1 tsp light soy	$1/8$ tsp pepper
1 tsp cornflour	

Method:

◆ Slice and marinate the chicken with the sesame paste, mustard and all the seasoning for 30 minutes.

◆ Stir in the beaten egg to mix well. Remove the excess marinade then coat evenly with the cornflour.

◆ Bring the oil to the boil in a very hot wok. Deep fry the chicken for approximately 4 minutes or until golden brown. Drain and leave to cool.

◆ Deep dry the chicken again for another minute then drain on absorbent paper. Cut into smaller pieces and dish. Garnish with carrot flower and the parsley. Serve with Worcestershire sauce and spicy salt.

添丁鸡酒
CHICKEN IN SWEET WINE

材料:

上鸡 1 只约 1500 克	木耳 30 克
猪肝 125 克	沸水 3 杯
上肉 125 克	姜 250 克
花生 1 杯	葱头 1 粒
油 2 汤匙	

腌鸡料:

姜汁 1/4 杯	生粉 1 汤匙
酒 1/4 杯	

腌肝料:

姜汁 1 茶匙	生粉 1 茶匙
酒 1 茶匙	

腌肉料:

生抽 1 茶匙	生粉 1/2 茶匙
糖 1/2 茶匙	水 2 汤匙
酒 1/2 茶匙	

调味:

糯米酒 3 杯	盐 1 茶匙
白酒 2 杯	糖 1 茶匙
上汤 4 杯	

制法:

- 鸡洗净切大件，放入腌鸡料中腌 30 分钟。
- 猪肝切大片，放入腌肝料中腌 30 分钟候用。
- 上肉切片，加入腌肉料内腌 20 分钟。
- 花生洗净浸 1/2 小时。木耳浸透修剪妥当后放于 2 杯沸水中飞水片刻，捞起冲冻隔干水份。
- 姜去皮洗净剁成组粒。葱头拍扁。
- 烧红锅加油煮沸，爆香葱头弃去，再加姜粒爆透，随即放入鸡件及花生兜炒 5 分钟。倒下两种酒再煮沸，转倒于另一深锅内加木耳续煮 30 分钟。
- 猪肝及肉片一同放入余下沸水中飞水捞后冲冻，加入鸡酒中再煮 5 分钟。试妥味后即可离火，取出热食。

Ingredients:

1 chicken, about 1500g	30g black fungus
125g pork liver	3 cups boiling water
125g lean pork	250g ginger
1 cup peanuts	1 shallot
2 tbsp corn oil	

Chicken Marinade:

1/4 cup ginger juice	1 tbsp cornflour
1/4 cup wine	

Liver Marinade:

1 tsp ginger juice	1 tsp cornflour
1 tsp wine	

Pork Marinade:

1 tsp light soy	1/2 tsp cornflour
1/2 tsp sugar	2 tbsp water
1/2 tsp wine	

Seasoning:

3 cups glutinous rice wine	4 cupa broth
2 cups white wine	1 tsp salt
	1 tsp sugar

Method:

- Clean and chop the chicken into bite-sized pieces. Soak in the mixed chicken marinade for 30 minutes.
- Slice and mix the liver with the liver marinade and set aside for 30 minutes.
- Slice the pork and stir in the mixed pork marinade and marinate for 20 minutes.
- Wash and soak the peanuts for half an hour. Soak, trim and blanch the black fungus in 2 cups of the boiling water for a minute. Refresh and drain.
- Scrape, wash and dice the ginger coarsely. Mash the shallot.
- Heat a wok and bring the oil to the boil. Saute the shallot until fragrant then discard. Add the ginger to saute well and stir in the chicken and nuts to fry for 5 minutes. Pour in both of the wines to bring to the boil. Transfer into a saucepan and simmer with the fungus for 30 minutes.
- Blanch the liver and pork in the remaining boiling water then refresh. Add into the chicken wine and continue to cook for a further 5 minutes. Season to taste. Remove and serve.

家乡焗鸡煲

CHICKEN, MUSHROOMS AND BLACK FUNGUS CASSEROLE

材料:

鸡 1/2 只约 500 克	沸水 2 杯
油 1/2 锅	金针 30 克
熟冬菇 60 克	姜 4 片
木耳 15 克	葱头 3 粒
葱丝 1 汤匙	

腌料:

姜汁 1 汤匙	生粉 1 汤匙
酒 1 汤匙	

调味:

酒 1 茶匙	盐 1/6 茶匙
冬菇水 1 杯	糖 2 茶匙
生抽 1 汤匙	胡椒粉 1/4 茶匙

制法:

◆ 鸡洗净斩件以腌料和匀腌 20 分钟泡暖油候用。

◆ 熟冬菇片开。木耳以沸水浸透修妥切开飞水，与冬菇一同捞匀。金针浸片刻剪去头尾。姜切丝。葱头切片。

◆ 瓦锅烧热加油 1 汤匙煮沸爆香姜、葱头。加入鸡件及其他配料略炒后，潵酒加冬菇水及调味料，盖上锅盖煮 10 分钟。试妥味后洒下葱丝，原锅上桌。

Ingredients:

1/2 chicken, about 500g	2 cups hot water
1/2 wok oil	30g dried lily
60g cooked	flowers
Chinese mushrooms	4 slices ginger
15g black	3 shallots
fungus	1 tbsp shredded chives

Marinade:

1 tbsp ginger juice	1 tbsp cornflour
1 tbsp wine	

Seasoning:

1 tsp wine	1/6 tsp salt
1 cup mushroom stock	2 tsp sugar
1 tbsp light soy	1/4 tsp pepper

Method:

◆ Wash, dry and chop the chicken into serving pieces. Coat with the mixed marinade for 20 minutes. Parboil in the warm oil and drain, leaving 1 tbsp for later use.

◆ Halve the mushrooms. Soak the black fungus in the hot water for 30 minutes. Trim, blanch and mix with the mushrooms. Saturate the lily flowers with water and set aside for 10 minutes. Remove and cut off both ends. Shred the ginger. Slice the shallots.

◆ Drop the oil in a casserole and saute the ginger and shallots till pungent. Add the chicken and all the ingredients to saute for a while then sizzle the wine; pour in the mushroom stock and seasoning. Cover and simmer for 10 minutes. Adjust the flavor to taste and scatter in the chives. Serve in the casserole.

西汁火局鸡腿

CHICKEN THIGHS IN TANGY SAUCE

材料:

鸡腿下段 4 只 500 克　　姜茸 1 汤匙
姜 30 克　　　　　　　　葱头茸 1 汤匙
葱头 30 克　　　　　　　油 2 汤匙
沸水 3 杯　　　　　　　蜜糖 3 汤匙
酒 2 汤匙　　　　　　　番茄片围边

腌料:

酒 1 汤匙　　　　　　　盐 $1/4$ 茶匙
姜汁 1 汤匙　　　　　　鸡粉 $1/2$ 茶匙
茄汁 4 汤匙　　　　　　糖 1 汤匙
喼汁 2 汤匙　　　　　　黑椒粉 $1/4$ 茶匙
生抽 1 汤匙　　　　　　油 1 汤匙 (后下)

制法:

◆ 鸡腿解冻洗净。姜去皮切片拍扁。葱头去衣亦拍扁。

◆ 焗炉预开 200℃。

◆ 沸水放煲中,将姜、葱及酒同倾入文火煮 10 分钟至出味。加入鸡腿飞水至鸡皮收紧 (约 30 秒钟),即可捞出放水龙头下冲洗干净。

◆ 腌料放深碟中拌溶,加入姜葱茸试妥味。将鸡腿放入反复数次至沾满汁液。放置一旁腌 $1/2$ 小时。反转再腌 $1/2$ 小时。

◆ 焗盘放锡纸一张以油搪匀,将鸡腿排入。置中格上焗 10 分钟,取出淋汁涂油反转再焗 5 分钟。再将鸡腿整只涂上蜜糖续焗 4 分钟即可上碟,以番茄片围边点缀。原汁淋在鸡腿上点食。

Ingredients:

4 chicken drumsticks, about 500g
30g ginger
30g shallots
3 cups boiling water
2 tbsp wine
1 tbsp minced ginger
1 tbsp minced shallots or onions
2 tbsp oil for greasing
3 tbsp honey
tomatoes slices for garnishing

Marinade:

1 tbsp wine
1 tbsp ginger juice
4 tbsp tomato ketchup
2 tbsp Worcestershire sauce
1 tbsp light soy
$1/4$ tsp salt
$1/2$ tsp chicken powder
1 tbsp sugar
$1/4$ tsp black pepper
1 tbsp oil, to be added last

Method:

◆ Defrost and wash the chicken drumsticks. Peel, slice and mash the ginger. Peel and mash the shallots.

◆ Preheat the oven to 200℃.

◆ Pour the boiling water into a saucepan together with the ginger, shallots and wine to simmer for 10 minutes until the liquid gives out its aroma. Slide in the drumsticks to blanch for about 30 seconds to tighten the skin. Remove and rinse under a cold running tap. Drain and dry with a towel.

◆ Prepare the marinade in a bowl and add the minced ginger and shallots. Adjust the flavour according to taste. Dip in the drumsticks to coat with the sauce evenly. Set aside to marinate for 30 minutes then turn over to marinate for another 30 minutes.

◆ Line the baking tray with a piece of aluminum foil and grease it with oil. Arrange the drumsticks on the tray and bake in the oven for 10 minutes. Take the tray out of the oven to pour the sauce on the meat then turn over to bake for another 5 minutes.

◆ Remove and brush the drumsticks with the honey and continue to bake for a final 4 minutes. Dish and garnish with the tomato slices. Pour the sauce from the baking tray on the drumsticks and serve hot.

烧酱爆鸡翼

CHICKEN WINGS IN CHA SHIU SAUCE

材料:

鸡翼 10 只　　　　　　蒜头 2 粒
姜 3 片　　　　　　　　葱粒 1 汤匙
葱头 2 粒

调味:

绍酒 1 汤匙　　　　　　麻酱 1 汤匙
上汤 1 杯　　　　　　　生抽 1 茶匙
柱侯酱 2 汤匙　　　　　糖 2 汤匙
海鲜酱 2 汤匙

制法:

◆ 鸡翼每只斩成 3 段,用沸水淋透,再以冷水洗净。然后隔干水份,用姜汁、酒各 2 汤匙,生粉 1 茶匙腌 30 分钟。

◆ 姜、葱、蒜头剁烂成茸候用。

◆ 调味酱料与姜、葱、蒜茸混和放碗中。将三分一加在鸡翼上捞匀,再腌 30 分钟。

◆ 烧红锅,放入油 2 汤匙煮沸。另投葱蒜头各 1 粒爆香,将酱料倒入再爆片刻。随即加入鸡翼兜炒,灒酒倒入上汤,盖上锅盖焗约 10 分钟。揭盖再炒匀至汁水将干时即可盛起,洒下葱粒上桌。

Ingredients:

10 chicken wings　　　2 garlic cloves
3 pieces ginger　　　　1 tbsp chopped spring
2 shallots　　　　　　onion

Seasoning:

1 tbsp sherry　　　　　2 tbsp sweet paste
1 cup stock　　　　　　1 tbsp sesame paste
2 tbsp groundbean　　　1 tsp light soy
paste　　　　　　　　2 tbsp sugar

Method:

◆ Section and blanch the chicken wings in boiling water. Refresh and drain. Marinate with 2 tbsp each of ginger juice and wine, and 1 tsp cornflour for 30 minutes.

◆ Mince ginger, shallot and garlic for further use.

◆ Mix seasoning with half of the mashed ginger, shallot and garlic. Stir $1/3$ of it into the chicken marinade to mix well. Continue to marinate for 30 minutes.

◆ Heat a wok to bring 2 tbsp oil to the boil. Saute remaining half of ginger, shallot and garlic until fragrant. Add the mixed seasoning to stir for a while. Pour in the chicken wings and saute thoroughly. Sizzle wine and add stock to simmer for 10 minutes. Remove lid to stir until sauce nearly dries. Sprinkle spring onion on top and serve.

盐水浸鸡翼

CHICKEN WINGS IN RICH SALINE SAUCE

材料:

鸡翼 1000 克　　　　葱 5 棵
水 10 杯　　　　　　酒 1/4 杯
八角 4 粒　　　　　　麻油 2 茶匙
姜 6 片　　　　　　　芫荽 2 棵

调味:

盐 1/2 杯　　　　　　糖 1/4 杯
鸡精 1 粒

制法:

◆ 鸡翼洗净，放于半锅沸水中飞水后，捞起洗净，浸在冻水中。
◆ 深锅一个，放入水 10 杯。加入八角、姜及调味煮 20 分钟试至合味。
◆ 鸡翼从冻水中捞出隔净水份，与葱及酒一同倒入沸盐水中。随即熄去炉火浸半小时。
◆ 将鸡翼捞起摊冻，涂以麻油上碟以芫荽装饰。

Ingredients:

1000g chicken wings　　5 spring onion
10 cups water　　　　　1/4 cup wine
4 star anise　　　　　　2 tsp sesame oil
6 slices ginger　　　　　2 sprigs parsley

Seasoning:

1/2 cup salt　　　　　　1/4 cup sugar
1 cube chicken essence

Method:

◆ Wash and blanch the chicken wings in a few cups of boiling water. Refresh.
◆ Soak the wings in iced water for 30 minutes and drain.
◆ Bring the water to the boil in a saucepan. Add the star anise, ginger and the seasoning to simmer over low heat for 20 minutes. Turn off the heat.
◆ Place the chicken wings, spring onion and wine in the sauce to soak for 30 minutes. Remove from the sauce to brush with sesame oil. Garnish with parsley and serve cold.

香葱焗鸡翼

CHICKEN WINGS WITH SPRING ONIONS

材料：

鸡翼 500 克	葱 5 棵
姜 4 片	红椒 1 只
葱头 10 粒	油 1 汤匙
蒜头 2 粒	

腌料：

姜汁 1 汤匙	糖 1 茶匙
酒 1 汤匙	生粉 1 茶匙
生抽 1 汤匙	

调味：

酒 1 茶匙	糖 2 茶匙
上汤 $2/3$ 杯	胡椒粉 $1/4$ 茶匙
生抽 1 汤匙	麻油 1 茶匙

制法：

◆ 鸡翼解冻后每边剥 3 刀，以沸水拖过抹干。加入混合腌料中拌匀腌 $1/2$ 小时，泡油候用。

◆ 姜拍扁。葱头、蒜头切片。葱切段。红椒切丝。

◆ 烧红锅，加油煮沸。放入姜、葱、蒜片爆香。倒下鸡翼拌匀，潵酒加上汤及调味料，盖上锅盖焗 5 分钟。揭盖加葱度抛匀上碟，洒红椒丝装饰。

Ingredients:

500g chicken wings	2 cloves garlic
4 slices ginger	5 spring onions
10 shallots	1 red chilli
	1 tbsp oil

Marinade:

1 tbsp ginger juice	1 tsp sugar
1 tbsp wine	1 tsp cornflour
1 tbsp light soy	

Seasoning:

1 tsp wine	2 tsp sugar
$2/3$ cup stock	$1/4$ tsp pepper
1 tbsp light soy	1 tsp sesame oil

Method:

◆ Defrost the chicken wings and cut 3 slashes on each side. Blanch in hot water for 1 minute and towel dry.

◆ Mix the marinade in a large bowl. Immerse the chicken in the marinade and set aside for 30 minutes. Parboil in warm oil over medium heat for 3 minutes.

◆ Mash the ginger. Slice the shallota and garlic. Section the spring onions. Shred the chilli.

◆ Heat a wok and bring the oil to the boil. Pour in the ginger, shallots and garlic and saute until fragrant. Slide in the chicken and fry for 4 minutes. Sizzle the wine, add the stock and season to taste. Cover and cook for 5 minutes. Remove the lid and stir in the spring onions. Dish and garnish with the chilli.

鸡丝扒苋菜

CHINESE SPINACH WITH SHREDDED CHICKEN

材料:

红苋菜 500 克   蒜 3 粒
鸡胸肉 125 克   葱头 1 粒
蛋白 1/2 只   油 2 汤匙
姜 2 片

腌料:

姜汁 1 茶匙   生粉 1/2 茶匙
酒 1 茶匙   胡椒粉 1/4 茶匙
蛋白 1/2 只

调味:

盐 1/2 茶匙   生抽 1 茶匙
糖 1/4 茶匙   胡椒粉 1/4 茶匙
酒 1 茶匙   麻油 1 茶匙
菜汁 1/4 杯   生粉水 1 茶匙

制法:

◆ 苋菜仔洗净摘妥, 以箕箕隔干水份。
◆ 鸡胸肉切丝, 腌 20 分钟, 泡油留用。
◆ 姜切丝, 蒜拍扁, 葱头切片。
◆ 烧红锅, 放入油煮沸, 爆香姜、蒜, 倒入苋菜猛兜数下。即干盐、糖炒匀, 盛在长碟中, 菜汁倒起留作上汤用。
◆ 另锅烧红, 以油爆香葱片, 瓒酒倒入菜汁煮沸, 加入调味料和匀, 以生粉水打芡将鸡丝倒入拌匀铲起, 淋在苋菜上即成。

Ingredients:

500g Chinese spinach	2 slices ginger
125g chicken breast	3 garlic cloves
	1 shallot
1/2 egg white	2 tbsp oil

Marinade:

1 tsp ginger juice	1/2 tsp cornflour
1 tep wine	1/4 tsp pepper
1/2 egg white	

Seasoning:

1/2 tsp salt	1 tsp light soy
1/4 tsp sugar	1/4 tap pepper
1 tsp wine	1 tsp sesame oil
1/4 cup stock	1 tsp cornflour mix

Method:

◆ Wash and trim the spinach. Drain.
◆ Shred and marinate the chicken for 20 minutes. Parboil in warm oil and drain.
◆ Shred the ginger. Mash the garlic and slice the shallot.
◆ Heat a wok to bring the oil to the boll. Saute the ginger and garlic until fragrant. Stir in the spinach to fry for 20 seconds. Sprinkle in the salt and sugar to mix well. Remove and squeeze out the excess water from vegetables and keep for use as the 1/4 cup stock. Arrange the spinach on a platter.
◆ Heat some oil in another wok. Saute the shallot. Sizzle wine and pour in the stock. Add the seasoning to taste. Thicken the gravy with cornflour solution. Mix in the chicken, then pour over the cooked spinach and serve hot.

香酥鸡件
CRISPY CHICKEN

材料：

鸡胸肉 500 克   自发粉 $^1/_2$ 杯
葱头茸 1 汤匙   香盐 1 茶匙
蒜头茸 1 茶匙   沸油 $^1/_2$ 锅
鸡蛋 1 只

腌料：

姜汁 2 汤匙   糖 1 汤匙
酒 2 汤匙   五香粉 1 汤匙
生抽 2 汤匙   黑椒粉 1 茶匙

制法：

◆ 鸡胸肉洗净去皮切大件，以刀两边剟花纹。
◆ 腌料和匀加入葱、蒜茸混合，将鸡件放入拌匀腌 $^1/_2$ 小时。每 10 分钟翻动一次。
◆ 蛋去壳打烂，加在鸡件上拌匀再腌 10 分钟。
◆ 自发粉与香盐和匀，将鸡件放入，每块沾满粉料，滑落沸油锅内炸至金黄色。捞起以纸吸去余油上碟。

Ingredients:

500g chicken breasts   1 egg
1 tbsp minced shallots $^1/_2$ cup self-raising flour
1 tsp minced garlic   1 tsp spicy salt
    $^1/_2$ wok oil

Marinade:

2 tbsp ginger juice   1 tbsp five-spice powder
2 tbsp wine
2 tbsp light soy   1 tsp black pepper
1 tbsp sugar

Method:

◆ Remove the chicken skin and chop the chicken into large pieces. Score crisscross patterns on both sides of the chicken breasts.
◆ Mix the marinade with the minced ingredients. Immerse the chicken in it for 30 minutes, turning over every 10 minutes to ensure even coverage.
◆ Beat the egg and add it to the chicken. Marinate for another 10 minutes.
◆ Mix the self-raising flour with the spicy salt and evenly coat the pieces of chicken. Bring the oil to the boil in wok. Slide in the chicken and deep fry until golden brown. Drain off the excess oil and serve.

柠檬软鸡
DEEP FRIED CHICKEN IN LEMON SAUCE

材料：

鸡胸2只各重180克　　炸油 $1/2$ 锅
蛋1只打烂　　　　　　柠檬2个
生粉1杯　　　　　　　芫荽2棵
油3汤匙

腌料：

姜汁1汤匙　　　　　　糖1茶匙
酒1汤匙　　　　　　　胡椒粉 $1/4$ 茶匙
生抽1汤匙　　　　　　生粉1茶匙

调味：

上汤 $1/2$ 杯　　　　　　胡椒粉 $1/4$ 茶匙
盐 $1/4$ 匙　　　　　　　麻油 $1/2$ 茶匙
醋3汤匙　　　　　　　酒1茶匙
糖2汤匙

芡料：

吉士粉2汤匙　　　　　水3汤匙
生粉 $1/2$ 茶匙

制法：

◆ 鸡胸去骨片成大薄片，放入腌料中腌30分钟。
◆ 鸡肉放入蛋液中拖匀，转放干生粉内上满粉以手按实。
◆ 烧红锅，倒入炸油煮沸。滑入鸡件炸至金黄色，捞起切件上碟。
◆ 柠檬1个榨汁加入全部调味料（酒除外）和匀。芫荽洗净摘妥放置一旁候用。
◆ 原锅烧热，将余油煮沸。溅酒加柠檬混合物试妥味。以吉士粉、生粉加水和匀慢慢流入煮成浓芡淋在炸鸡上。
◆ 另1个柠檬切片与芫荽同放碟边点缀。

Ingredients:

2 chicken breasts　　　2 lemons
about 180g each　　　2 parsley sprigs
1 beaten egg　　　　　3 tbsp oil
1cup cornflour
$1/2$ wok oil for deep
frying

Chicken Marinade:

1 tbsp ginger juice　　1 tsp sugar
1 tbsp wine　　　　　$1/4$ tsp pepper
1 tbsp light soy　　　1 tsp cornflour

Seasoning:

$1/2$ cup stock　　　　　$1/4$ tsp pepper
$1/4$ tsp salt　　　　　　$1/2$ tsp sesame oil
3 tbsp vinegar　　　　1 tsp wine
2 tbsp sugar

Gravy Mix:

2 tbsp custard powder　3 tbsp water
$1/2$ tsp cornflour

Method:

◆ Debone and slice the chicken into large thin pieces then immerse in the marinade for 30 minutes.
◆ Toss the chicken in the beaten egg then coat evenly with the cornflour.
◆ Heat a wok until very hot and pour in the oil to bring to the boil. Slide in the chicken to deep fry until golden brown. Drain, cut and dish. Leaving 2 tbsp oil in the wok for later use.
◆ Squeeze out the juice of one lemon and mix with all the seasoning except the wine. Wash and trim the parsleys and set aside for later use.
◆ Reheat the wok and bring the remaining oil to the boil. Sizzle the wine then pour in the lemon mixture and season to taste. Mix the custard powder and cornflour with the water then stream into the sauce to thicken. Pour over the chicken.
◆ Slice the other lemon and arrange round the platter with the parsley.

酥炸五香鸡
DEEP FRY SPICY CHICKEN

材料:

鸡腿 4 只	葱头茸 2 汤匙
五香粉 3 汤匙	蒜头茸 2 汤匙
胡椒粉 $1/2$ 茶匙	蛋 1 只
姜茸 2 汤匙	生粉 $1/2$ 杯

调味:

姜汁 2 汤匙	生抽 3 汤匙
白酒 2 汤匙	生粉 1 茶匙
糖 2 汤匙	麻油 2 茶匙

制法:

◆ 鸡腿洗净抹干, 每只分切二段, 以刀在皮肉上剥三刀, 然后再用刀将鸡腿拍扁。

◆ 姜汁及酒放在深碟上, 将鸡腿放入沾匀腌 20 分钟。

◆ 五香粉、胡椒粉、姜、葱、蒜茸与其余调味料和匀倒在鸡腿上拌匀再腌 1 小时。每 15 分钟转身 1 次。

◆ 蛋打烂加入腌料中和匀, 再放在生粉碟中卷满粉料。

◆ 烧红锅加油约 8 杯煮沸, 将鸡腿放入文火炸至金黄色。捞起隔净余油上碟。

Ingredients:

4 chicken thighs	2 tbsp mashed shallot
3 tbsp five spice powder	2 tbsp mashed garlic
$1/2$ tsp pepper	1 egg
2 tbsp mashed ginger	$1/2$ cup cornflour

Seasoning:

2 tbsp ginger juice	3 tbsp light soy
2 tbsp white wine	1 tsp cornflour
2 tbsp sugar	2 tsp sesame oil

Method:

◆ Wash and dry the chicken thigh. Cut each thigh into halves. Slash 3 to 4 cuts onto each pieces of meat, and pat with the side of a chopper.

◆ Place the ginger juice and wine into a saucer and marinate the chicken for 20 minutes.

◆ Mix the five spice powder, pepper, ginger, shallot, garlic and remaining seasoning together and pour over the chicken to marinate for another hour. Turn the chicken every 15 minutes to soak evenly.

◆ Beat the egg and add into the chicken marinade to mix thoroughly. Dust the chicken with cornflour.

◆ Heat a wok to bring 8 cups of oil to the boil. Put in the chicken to deep fry over medium heat until golden. Remove and drain. Dish and serve.

杂果鸡粒
DICED CHICKEN WITH MIXED FRUIT

材料：

鸡腿肉 250 克　　　　青提子 90 克
菠萝 90 克　　　　　　姜 1 片
盐水 1 杯　　　　　　　葱 2 棵
番茄 90 克　　　　　　油 2 汤匙
荔枝 90 克

腌料：

姜汁 2 茶匙　　　　　糖 1 茶匙
酒 1 茶匙　　　　　　水 2 汤匙
生抽 1 汤匙　　　　　油 1 汤匙（后下）
生粉 1 茶匙

调味：

盐 $1/4$ 茶匙　　　　　生抽 2 茶匙
糖 1 茶匙　　　　　　胡椒粉 $1/8$ 茶匙
酒 1 茶匙　　　　　　麻油 1 茶匙

制法：

◆ 鸡腿肉去皮切 2 公分丁方粒，以深碗盛之。将腌料和匀倾入拌匀腌 20 分钟。把油搞入拌匀再腌 20 分钟。

◆ 菠萝预先用盐水浸 1 小时，冲净抹干切粒。番茄切粒。荔枝去壳去核每个分切四份。青提子去核洗净。姜切成小片。葱切粒。

◆ 烧红锅加油 1 汤匙煮沸。放入姜片爆香，即下腌透鸡肉兜炒约 1 分钟，以碟盛起。

◆ 再烧热另一只锅或煎锅，加入其余 1 汤匙油煮沸。倒下番茄及菠萝，加部分盐，糖兜匀。随将鸡粒重倒入锅内，灒酒将全部调味加入拌匀。最后再加荔枝、提子，停火捞匀洒葱粒上碟。

Ingredients :

250g chicken meat　　　90g lychees
90g pineapples　　　　　90g grapes
1 cup salted water　　　1 slice ginger
90g tomatoes　　　　　　2 spring onions
　　　　　　　　　　　　2 tbsp oil

Chicken Marinade:

2 tsp ginger juice　　　1 tsp sugar
1 tsp wine　　　　　　　2 tbsp water
1 tbsp light soy　　　　1 tbsp oil, to be added
1 tap cornflour　　　　　last

Seasoning:

$1/4$ tsp salt　　　　　　2 tsp light soy
1 tsp sugar　　　　　　$1/8$ tsp pepper
1 tsp wine　　　　　　　1 tsp sesame oil

Method:

◆ Discard the skin of the chicken meat and dice into 2 cm cubes. Place the diced chicken in a bowl and blend in the marinade. Set aside for 20 minutes. Add the oil and continue to marinate for a further 20 minutes.

◆ Presoak the pineapples in the salted water for 1 hour. Refresh, pat dry and dice. Dice the tomatoes. Shell, core and quarter the lychees. Deseed and wash the grapes. Slice the ginger into tiny slivers. Dice the spring onions.

◆ Heat a frying pan to bring 1 tbsp oil to the boil. Saute the ginger and put in the chicken meat to stir fry for about 1 minute. Dish.

◆ Heat another pan to bring the remaining 1 tbsp oil to boil. Pour in the tomatoes and pineapples with half of the salt and sugar to stir well. Return the chicken meat into the pan. Sizzle the wine and blend in the seasoning. Turn off the heat then add the lychees and grapes to toss thoroughly. Sprinkle the spring onions and dish.

茄汁鸡丁

DICED CHICKEN WITH TOMATO KETCHUP

材料:

鸡腿 1 只约 300 克   洋葱 1 只约 125 克
盐水 2 杯   油 2 汤匙
青豆 $^3/_4$ 杯

腌鸡料:

姜汁 1 茶匙   生粉 1 茶匙
酒 1 茶匙   茄汁 1 汤匙
生抽 1 茶匙   水 2 汤匙
糖 $^1/_2$ 茶匙   油 1 汤匙（后下）

调味:

鸡粉 $^1/_4$ 茶匙   茄汁 2 汤匙
生粉 $^1/_2$ 茶匙   喼汁 1 汤匙
温水 $^1/_4$ 杯   糖 1 茶匙
盐 $^1/_4$ 茶匙

制法:

◆ 鸡腿洗净去骨切成丁。
◆ 将全部腌鸡料放在碗中和匀。倒入鸡丁拌匀腌半小时，将油拌入再腌 20 分钟。
◆ 盐水放小煲中煮沸，将青豆放入煮片刻。取出以水冲冻。隔干水份候用。
◆ 洋葱去衣洗净切粒。
◆ 锅烧红，将 1 汤匙油放入爆香洋葱粒。盛起置一旁晾凉。
◆ 余下油 1 汤匙倾入原锅中将鸡丁滑下爆至变色后，即将青豆、洋葱拌入。
◆ 鸡精及生粉溶于温水内再加其余调味料搞溶。倒入小煲中煮稠。加在鸡丁、青豆、洋葱粒上兜匀上碟。

Ingredients:

1 chicken thigh, about 300g $^3/_4$ cup sweet peas
2 cups salted water   125g onions
2 tbsp oil

Chicken Marinade:

1 tsp ginger juice   1 tbsp tomato ketchup
1 tsp wine   2 tbsp water
1 tsp light soy   1 tbsp oil, to be added
$^1/_2$ tsp sugar   last
1 tsp cornflour

Seasoning:

$^1/_4$ tsp chicken essence   2 tbsp tomato ketchup
$^1/_2$ tep cornflour   1 tbsp Worcestershire
$^1/_4$ cup warm water   sauce
$^1/_4$ tsp salt   1 tsp sugar

Method:

◆ Debone, wash and dice the chicken thigh.
◆ Prepare the above marinade, except the oil, in a bowl and put in the chicken to marinate for 30 minutes. Blend in the oil and continue to marinate for another 20 minutes.
◆ Bring the salted water to boil in a small saucepan and pour in the peas to cook for 10 seconds. Remove and rinse under a running tap until cooled. Drain and set aside for later use.
◆ Peel, wash and dice the onions.
◆ Heat the wok with 1 tbsp oil to saute the onions. Dish and set aside to cool.
◆ Heat the remaining oil in a wok and slide in the chicken to stir fry until the chicken meat turns white. Stir in the sweet peas and onions to mix well.
◆ Dissolve the chicken essence and cornflour in the warm water and mix well with the remaining seasoning. Simmer in a small saucepan until the sauce thickens. Pour over the chicken, sweet peas and onions to mix thoroughly. Dish and serve.

核桃鸡米
DICED CHICKEN WITH WALNUTS

材料：

鸡柳 250 克　　　　　姜葱蒜茸各 1 茶匙
芹菜 60 克　　　　　　红椒粒 1 茶匙
去衣核桃 1/2 杯　　　　海鲜酱 2 汤匙
生菜 1 棵

腌料：

姜汁 1 茶匙　　　　　生粉 1 茶匙
酒 1 茶匙　　　　　　水 2 汤匙
盐 1/4 茶匙　　　　　油 1 茶匙
糖 1/2 茶匙

调味：

酒 1 茶匙　　　　　　胡椒粉 1/4 茶匙
上汤 1/4 杯　　　　　生粉水 1 茶匙
生抽 2 茶匙　　　　　麻油 1 茶匙
糖 1 茶匙

制法：

◆ 鸡洗净切粒，以混合腌料腌 10 分钟后泡嫩油捞起候用。
◆ 芹菜洗净切粒。核桃用沸水略浸后以冻油浸炸至金黄色，隔油切粒。生菜洗净修剪成圆片。
◆ 烧红锅加油 2 汤匙爆香姜、葱、蒜茸。放入鸡粒、芹菜粒炒片刻。灒酒加上汤及混合调味料，倾入核桃及红椒粒炒数下，试妥味洒麻油上碟。
◆ 食时将鸡粒放在生菜叶上，再加海鲜酱即成。

Ingredients:

250g chicken fillets　　　　1 tsp minced shallot
60g celery　　　　　　　　1 tsp minced garlic
1/2 cup peeled walnuts　　 1 tsp diced red chillies
1 head of lettuce　　　　　2 tbsp Hoi Sin/
1 tsp minced ginger　　　　barbeque sauce

Marinade :

1 tsp ginger juice　　　　1 tsp cornflour
1 tsp wine　　　　　　　 2 tbsp water
1/4 tsp salt　　　　　　　1 tsp oil
1/2 tsp sugar

Seasoning:

1 tsp wine　　　　　　　 1/4 tsp pepper
1/4 cup stock　　　　　　 1/2 tsp cornflour +
2 tsp light soy　　　　　 1/2 tsp water
1 tsp sugar　　　　　　　1 tsp sesame oil

Method:

◆ Dice the chicken and soak in the marinade for 10 minutes. Parboil in warm oil and drain.
◆ Dice the celery. Soak the walnuts in hot water briefly, dry thoroughly and put in warm oil and slowly deep fry them until golden brown and dice. Wash and trim the lettuce leaves.
◆ Bring 2 tbsp of oil to the boil and saute the minced ingredients until fragrant. Pour in the chicken and celery. Sizzle the wine and add the seasoning. Adjust the flavour to taste. Scatter the walnuts and chillies on top; sprinkle in the sesame oil and serve with the lettuce leaves and Hoi Sin sauce.
◆ Put a spoonful of the diced ingredients on the lettuce leaf, add a little Hoi Sin sauce, wrap up the leaf and eat it.

双丝粉皮

Mung Bean Sheet with Ham and Chicken

材料:

粉皮 3 块	火腿 90 克
暖水 3 杯	熟鸡肉 90 克
沸水 2 杯	番茄 3 只
麻油 1 茶匙	青椒 1 只点缀

调味:

麻油 1 茶匙	芝麻酱 2 汤匙
生抽 1 汤匙	豆瓣酱 1 汤匙
糖 2/3 汤匙	上汤 1/4 杯

制法:

◆ 粉皮用暖水浸软，切成 1.25 公分条。用沸水淋过隔干水份，以麻油捞匀排放碟上。

◆ 火腿与熟鸡肉分别切粗条。番茄切片。青椒切花。

◆ 番茄片排放在粉皮上成一圆形，圆形中放下火腿及鸡丝。青椒插在中央。

◆ 调味料放碗中和匀试至合味淋在肉上。食时全部捞匀。

Ingredients:

3 mung bean sheets	90g cooked
3 cups warm water	chicken
2 cups boiling water	3 tomatoes
1 tsp sesame oil	1 green chilli
90g ham	

Seasoning:

1 tsp sesame oil	1 tbsp hot broad bean
1 tbsp light soy	paste
2/3 tbsp sugar	1/4 cup stock
2 tbsp sesame paste	

Method:

◆ Immerse the mung bean sheets in the warm water for 30 minutes. Cut into 1.25 cm strips when soft. Scald with the boiling water and drain. Mix evenly with the sesame oil then arrange on a platter.

◆ Shred the ham and chicken. Slice the tomatoes. Cut the chilli to make a chilli tassel for garnishing.

◆ Halve the tomato slices and arrange in a circle on the mung bean strips. Place the ham and chicken in the centre of the tomato circle. Garnish with the chilli.

◆ Mix the seasoning thoroughly in a small bowl and pour over the meat. Stir well before eating.

白切鸡
POACHED CHICKEN

材料:

水 20 杯　　　　　　　麻油涂面
上鸡 1 只约 1500 克

调味:

姜汁 2 汤匙　　　　　　盐 2 汤匙
酒 2 汤匙　　　　　　　糖 1 汤匙

蘸料:

姜 30 克　　　　　　　糖 1 茶匙
葱茸 15 克　　　　　　沸油 2 汤匙
盐 2 汤匙

制法:

◆ 深锅内放清水煮沸。加入姜汁、酒、盐及糖
　 试妥味后随将洗净之鸡放入，待水煮沸时，
　 停火盖上锅盖浸 30 分钟。

◆ 将鸡取出，置水龙头下不断冲水约 30 分钟，
　 滴干水份，以毛巾抹干。涂以麻油后斩件上
　 碟，排成鸡之原状。

◆ 姜洗净磨成茸，放在小碟中，加葱茸、幼盐、
　 糖捞匀，潸下沸油，即可与鸡同上。

Ingredients:

20 cups water　　　　sesame oil for brushing
1 chicken, about 1500g

Seasoning:

2 tbsp ginger juice　　2 tbsp salt
2 tbsp wine　　　　　1 tbsp sugar

Dipping:

30g ginger　　　　　2 tbep salt
15g chopped　　　　1 tsp sugar
chives　　　　　　　2 tbsp hot oil

Method:

◆ Bring the water to the boil in a deep saucepan. Season with the ginger juice, wine, salt and sugar. Clean the chicken and put into the cleaned seasoned water. Reboil and turn off the heat. Leave the chicken to soak in the hot soup with the lid on for 30 minutes.

◆ Remove the chicken and place under a running tap to refresh for 30 to 60 minutes. Drain and dry with a towel. Brush the sesame oil over the whole carcass then chop into serving pieces. Arrange into the original shape of a chicken on a platter.

◆ Clean and grate the ginger to put in a small dish. Add the chopped chives, salt, sugar and the hot oil to mix well and serve as a dipping.

梅子烧鸡

ROAST CHICKEN WITH PRESERVED PRUNES

材料:

鸡 1 只约 1500 克	红椒 1 只
姜汁 2 汤匙	油 3 汤匙
酒 2 汤匙	蒜茸 2 汤匙
酸梅 180 克	磨豉酱 2 汤匙
冰糖 150 克	老抽 1 汤匙

调味:

上汤 1 杯	糖 1 茶匙
盐 1 茶匙	玫瑰露 1 茶匙

制法:

◆ 鸡洗净抹干水份,以姜汁酒将鸡涂匀内外。

◆ 酸梅去核剁烂。冰糖压碎,红椒切丝。

◆ 烧红锅加油 1 汤匙爆香蒜茸,倒下磨豉酱、酸梅、冰糖及红椒煮片刻盛起放入鸡肚内,以针将开口处缝合。

◆ 用老抽将鸡外皮涂匀,再将余油烧沸把鸡放入,煎至金黄色,以焗架盛起。

◆ 烧盘内放上汤、盐及酒。置已预热200℃之焗炉内焗约25分钟至两边金黄色。取出晾凉斩件砌回鸡形。

◆ 将鸡腹内梅子酱倒出,与烤盘内之汁混和,淋在已斩之鸡件上。

Ingredients:

1 chicken, about 1500g	1 red chilli
2 tbsp gainger juice	3 tbsp oil
2 tbsp wine	2 tbsp minced garlic
180g preserved prunes	2 tbsp ground bean paste
150g rock sugar	1 tbsp dark soy

Seasoning:

1 cup stock	1 tsp sugar
1 tsp salt	1 tsp rose wine

Method:

◆ Clean and towel dry the chicken thoroughly. Rub the inside and outside of the chicken with the ginger juice and wine. Leave aside for later use. Remove the stones and mash the preserved prunes. Crush the rock sugar and shred the red chilli.

◆ Heat a wok with 1 tbsp oil to saute the garlic until aromatic. Stir in the bean paste and fry for 20 seconds. Add the stoned prunes, rock sugar and red chilli and cook into a puree. Spoon the puree inside the chicken and then seal up the opening with a skewer.

◆ Rub the dark soy on to the chicken skin then shallow fry in the remaining oil until golden. Place on a rack over a baking tray.

◆ Fill the baking tray with 1 cup stock. Add the salt and wine then put into a preheated oven of about 200℃ and bake for 25 minutes until both sides are golden brown.

◆ Remove the chicken from the oven and drain the sauce from the inside. Chop the chicken into small pieces and arrange them back into the shape of a chicken. Mix the sauce thoroughly with the stock in the tray and pour over the chopped chicken. Garnish with a carrot or tomato rose and parsley.

盐火局鸡翼
SALT-BAKED CHICKEN WINGS

材料：

鸡翼 10 只　　　　老抽 2 汤匙
姜茸 1 汤匙　　　　纱纸数张
葱茸 1 汤匙　　　　粗盐 3000 克
八角茸 1 汤匙　　　芫荽装饰

调味：

香盐 1 茶匙　　　　生抽 2 茶匙
糖 1 茶匙　　　　　砂姜粉 1 茶匙

制法：

◆ 鸡翼洗净抹干，每边剥开二三刀。用姜汁、
　酒各 2 汤匙拌匀腌 1/2 小时。加入姜、葱、八
　角茸及全部调味料搞溶，再腌 1/2 小时。
◆ 每只鸡翼用老抽上色。
◆ 纱纸剪成约 12 英寸丁方，以油浸透后取出。
　每只鸡翼放在一方纱纸上包好。
◆ 烧红锅，倒入盐炒至大热时，将盐扒开把鸡
　翼逐包放入以热盐焗住。熄去炉火焗 15 至 20
　分钟。取出除去纱纸抹去腌料。以麻油擦匀
　在每只翼上，上碟。

Ingredients:

10 chicken wings　　　2 tbsp dark soy
1 tbsp minced ginger　few sheet paper
1 tbsp minced spring　2000g sea salt
onion　　　　　　　　parsley to garnish
1 tbsp minced star
anise

Seasoning:

1 tsp spicy salt　　　2 tsp light soy
1 tsp sugar　　　　　1 tsp ginger powder

Method:

◆ Wash and dry the chicken wings. Slash a few cuts
　on each side of the wing. Marinate with 2 tbsp each
　of ginger juice and wine for 30 minutes. Mix in
　the minced ginger, spring onion, star anise and
　seasoning. Continue to marinate for a further 30
　minutes.
◆ Colour each chicken wing with dark soy.
◆ Cut paper into 12 in. squares. Soak in oil for a while
　and remove onto a table. Place the wing onto the
　paper and wrap up securely.
◆ Heat a wok to parch the salt until very hot. Make a
　well in the centre to place in the chicken wing
　packets. Cover up with hot salt. Turn off the heat
　and leave to bake for 15 to 20 minutes. Remove
　the paper and wipe each wing with towel. Brush
　with sesame oil and dish.

蜜桃龙凤片

SAUTEED CHICKEN AND PRAWNS WITH PEACHES

材料：

鸡胸肉 150 克 　　　罐装桃 4 件
中虾 300 克 　　　　姜 2 片
生粉 1 茶匙 　　　　蒜头 1 粒
胡椒粉 1/4 茶匙 　　　葱 2 条
西芹 125 克

腌料：

姜汁 1 汤匙 　　　　生粉 1/2 茶匙
酒 1 汤匙 　　　　　蛋白 1/2 只
生抽 1 茶匙

调味：

盐 1/4 茶匙 　　　　糖 1 茶匙
酒 1 茶匙 　　　　　生粉水 1 茶匙
上汤 2 汤匙 　　　　麻油 1/2 茶匙
生抽 2 茶匙

制法：

◆ 鸡肉切成大薄片，放入拌好之腌料中和匀腌
　 1 小时。
◆ 虾去壳挑肠洗净。以利刀片成薄双飞片。将
　 生粉、胡椒粉捞匀洒在虾肉上。西芹撕妥与
　 边桃同切片。姜蒜头切指甲片，葱切度。
◆ 烧红锅将 4 杯油倾下煮至微热，即把鸡片滑
　 入用筷子拌匀。随即滑入虾肉以筷子拌开。
　 至肉片变色时，即以炸篱盛起隔净油。
◆ 另锅烧红，加油 2 汤匙煮沸洒盐爆香姜、蒜
　 片。加入西芹略炒后，将鸡片、虾片倒入迅
　 速兜匀。灒酒倾入已和匀之调味料，再加桃
　 片、葱度猛炒数下即可上碟。

Ingredients:

150g chicken breasts	125g celery
300g medium sized prawns	4 pieces tinned peach
1 tsp cornflour	2 slices ginger
1/4 tsp pepper	1 garlic clove
	2 spring onions

Marinade:

1 tbsp ginger juice	1/2 tsp cornflour
1 tbep wine	1/2 egg white
1 tsp light soy	

Seasoning:

1/4 tsp salt	1 tsp sugar
1 tsp wine	1 tsp cornflour mix
2 tbsp stock	1/2 tsp sesame oil
2 tbsp light soy	

Method:

◆ Slice the chicken breasts into large thin pieces and immerse in the mixed marinade for 1 hour.
◆ Shell, devein and wash the prawns. Slice each prawn into butterfly pieces with a sharp knife. Coat with the cornflour and pepper. Trim and cut the celery. Slice the peaches and the garlic. Shred the ginger and section the spring onions.
◆ Heat 4 cups of oil in a wok until just warm. Slide in the chicken, loosen with a pair of chopsticks and then add the prawns. Parboil both the chicken and prawns until the colour has changed. Remove and drain.
◆ Clean and reheat the wok with 2 tbsp oil. Sprinkle the salt and add the ginger, garlic and celery to saute well. Stir in the chicken and prawns and fry briskly. Sizzle the wine, pour in the mixed seasoning and then add the peached and spring onions. Toss thoroughly and dish.

西椒豆豉鸡

SAUTEED CHICKEN IN BLACK BEAN SAUCE

材料：

上鸡¹/₂只约500克	豆豉酱2汤匙
油¹/₂锅	干葱头10粒
红椒2只	蒜头2粒
青椒2只	姜1片
	葱1棵

腌料：

姜汁2汤匙	生粉2汤匙
酒2汤匙	

调味：

酒1茶匙	生抽1汤匙
上汤¹/₂杯	糖2茶匙

制法：

◆ 鸡洗净抹干斩件。以和匀腌料腌20分钟。

◆ 油烧热后，将鸡滑入泡至七成熟。捞起隔去油。

◆ 红、青椒去籽切件。葱蒜头拍扁。姜剁茸，葱切度。

◆ 锅烧红，加油1汤匙煮沸，投下葱、蒜头、姜茸、豆豉酱爆香。跟着加入青红椒及鸡件稍兜。潜酒加上汤及调味料。盖上锅盖焗5分钟。揭盖加葱度拌匀上碟。

Ingredients:

¹/₂ chicken, about 500g	10 shallots
¹/₂ wok warm oil	2 garlic cloves
2 red chillies	1 slice ginger
2 green capsicums	1 spring onion
2 tbsp preaerved black bean paste	

Marinade:

2 tbsp ginger juice	2 tbsp cornflour
2 tbsp wine	

Seasoning:

1 tbsp wine	1 tbsp light soy
¹/₂ cup stock	2 tsp sugar

Method:

◆ Wash, dry and chop the chicken into serving pieces. Immerse in the marinade and set aside for 20 minutes.

◆ Parboil the chicken in the warm oil and drain. Leave 1 tbsp of oil for sauteeing.

◆ Deseed and wedge the chillies and capsicums. Mash the shallots and garlic. Mince the ginger. Section the spring onion.

◆ Heat the wok to bring the retained oil to the boil. Saute the shallots, garlic, ginger and the black bean paste until fragrant. Add the capsicums and chicken to stir fry rapidly. Sizzle the wine, add the stock and simmer for 5 minutes. Adjust the flavour to taste. Scatter in the spring onion then dish.

子萝鸡片

Sauteed Chicken with Ginger and Pineapple

材料：

鸡柳 180 克	姜丝 1 茶匙
酸姜 60 克	葱头片 1 汤匙
菠萝 60 克	蒜片 1 汤匙
青椒 1 只	葱度 2 汤匙
红椒 1 只	

腌料：

姜汁 1 茶匙	糖 $^1/_2$ 茶匙
酒 1 茶匙	蛋白半只
生抽 1 茶匙	麻油 1 茶匙
生粉 1 茶匙	

调味：

酒 $^1/_2$ 汤匙	胡椒粉 $^1/_8$ 茶匙
上汤 2 汤匙	生粉水 $^2/_3$ 茶匙
生抽 1 茶匙	麻油 1 茶匙
糖 $^1/_2$ 茶匙	

制法：

◆ 鸡柳洗净切片，以和匀腌料腌 10 分钟，泡嫩油候用。

◆ 酸姜、菠萝切片，青红椒去籽切件。

◆ 烧红锅放下油 1 汤匙爆香姜、葱、蒜片。加入青红椒兜炒数下。即落子姜、菠萝、鸡片快手拌匀。

◆ 灒酒把其余调味料混和倒入锅中抛匀，洒葱度上碟。

Ingredients :

180g chicken fillet	1 red chillies
60g pickled ginger	1 tsp shredded ginger
60g pineapple	1 tbsp sliced shallot
1 green capsicum	1 tbsp sliced garlic
	2 tbsp sectioned spring onion

Marinade:

1 tsp ginger juice	$^1/_2$ tsp sugar
1 tsp wine	$^1/_2$ egg white
1 tsp light soy	1 tsp sesame oil
1 tsp cornflour	

Seasoning :

$^1/_2$ tbsp wine	$^1/_8$ tsp pepper
2 tbsp stock	$^2/_3$ tsp cornflour mix
1 tsp light soy	1 tsp sesame oil
$^1/_2$ tsp sugar	

Method:

◆ Wash and slice chicken. Immerse in the mixed marinade and set aside for 10 minutes. Parboil in warm oil then drain.

◆ Slice the ginger and pineapple. Deseed and slice capsicum and chilli.

◆ Heat a wok to bring 1 tbsp oil to the boil. Saute the ginger, shallot and garlic until fragrant. Pour in the capsicum and chilli to fry for 10 seconds. Add the ginger, pineapple and chicken to saute rapidly.

◆ Sizzle wine then mix the seasoning and stream into the wok. Toss thoroughly with the spring onion. Dish and serve hot.

银果鸡丁

SAUTEED CHICKEN WITH GINKGO NUTS

材料：

鸡胸 375 克　　　　　青椒 1 只
暖油 4 杯　　　　　　红椒 2 只
去壳白果 90 克　　　　姜 2 片
马蹄 8 粒　　　　　　葱头 2 粒
熟冬菇 5 只　　　　　蒜头 2 粒

腌料：

姜汁 1 汤匙　　　　　糖 1/2 茶匙
酒 1 汤匙　　　　　　生粉 1 茶匙
盐 1/4 茶匙　　　　　油 1 汤匙

调味：

盐 1/4 茶匙　　　　　糖 1/2 茶匙
酒 1 茶匙　　　　　　生粉水 1 茶匙
上汤 1/2 杯　　　　　麻油 1/2 茶匙
生抽 2 茶匙

制法：

◆ 鸡胸去骨切粗粒，放入和匀腌料内腌 20 分钟，再拌入油续腌 20 分钟，置暖油内以中火泡 30 秒钟，盛起隔清余油，留起油 1 汤匙作起锅用。

◆ 白果置沸水中浸 1 分钟，去衣，马蹄去皮与冬菇齐切粒。青红椒去籽亦切粒。姜切丝，葱蒜头切片。

◆ 锅中余油烧沸，酒盐爆香姜、葱、蒜头，加入鸡肉及其他材料兜炒片刻。溅酒倾入上汤及调味料，慢慢流入生粉水打芡，滴入麻油拌匀即可上碟。

Ingredients:

375g chicken breasts　　　1 green capsicum
4 cups warm oil　　　　　2 red chillies
90g shelled ginkgo nuts　　2 slices ginger
8 water chestnuts　　　　　2 shallots
5 cooked Chinese mushrooms　2 cloves garlic

Marinade:

1 tbsp ginger juice　　　1/2 tsp sugar
1 tbsp wine　　　　　　1 tsp cornflour
1/4 tsp salt　　　　　　1 tbsp oil

Seasoning:

1/4 tsp salt　　　　　　1/2 tsp sugar
1 tsp wine　　　　　　1/2 tsp cornflour +
1/2 cup stock　　　　　1/2 tsp water
2 tsp light soy　　　　　1/2 tsp sesame oil

Method:

◆ Dice the chicken and soak in the marinade for 20 minutes. Blend in the oil to marinate for another 20 minutes. Parboil in warm oil and drain. Retain 1 tbsp of the oil for later use.

◆ Blanch the ginkgo nuts for 1 minute, then peel and set aside. Dice the water chestnuts, mushrooms, capsicum and chillies. Shred the ginger and slice the shallots and garlic.

◆ Reheat the oil in the wok. Sprinkle in the salt and saute the ginger, shallots and garlic until aromatic. Add all the ingredients and toss well. Sizzle the wine, trickle in the seasoning and adjust the flavour to taste. Dish and serve.

菜软鸡球

SAUTEED CHICKEN WITH GREEN VEGETABLES

材料:

鸡柳 250 克	红萝卜花 12 片
暖油 3 杯	姜 1 厚片
菜软 180 克	葱头 1 粒
盐水 3 杯	蒜头 1 粒

腌料:

姜汁 1 汤匙	生粉 1 茶匙
酒 1 汤匙	糖 1/2 茶匙
水 1 汤匙	麻油 1 茶匙
生抽 1 茶匙	

调味:

盐 1/4 茶匙	蚝油 2 茶匙
酒 1 茶匙	糖 1/2 茶匙
上汤 1/4 杯	胡椒粉 1/4 茶匙
生抽 1 茶匙	生粉水 1 茶匙

制法:

◆ 鸡柳洗净切 0.6 公分厚件, 用和匀腌料腌 30 分钟。泡暖油候用。

◆ 菜软洗净修好与红罗卜片置煮沸之盐水中加油及鸡粉少许一拖, 捞起冲冻水后再隔去水份。

◆ 姜、葱头、蒜头切薄片。

◆ 再烧红锅加油汤匙将姜、葱、蒜片及盐爆香。倒入菜软及红罗卜花加入鸡球炒数下。灒酒加上汤及调味料试妥味以生粉水埋芡兜匀上碟。红萝卜花装饰。

Ingredients :

250g chicken fillets	3 cups salted water
3 cups warm oil	12 pieces sliced carrot
180g green vegetables	1 thick sliced ginger
	1 shallot
	1 garlic

Marinade:

1 tbsp ginger juice	1 tsp cornflour
1 tbsp wine	1/2 tsp sugar
1 tbsp water	1 tsp sesame oil
1 tsp light soy	

Seasoning:

1/4 tsp salt	2 tsp oyster sauce
1 tsp wine	1/2 tsp sugar
1/4 cup stock	1/4 tsp pepper
1 tsp light soy	1 tsp cornflour mix

Method:

◆ Clean and cut the chicken fillets into bite-sized pieces of about 0.6 cm thick. Immerse in the marinade and set aside for 30 minutes.

◆ Heat a wok, put in the warm oil and parboil the chicken for 1 minute. Remove and drain.

◆ Wash and trim the vegetables. Bring the salted water to the boil and add a little oil and chicken powder. Blanch the vegetables and carrot pieces and drain.

◆ Cut the ginger into thin pieces. Slice the shallot and garlic.

◆ Heat a wok with 1 tbsp oil. Saute the ginger, shallot, garlic and salt until aromatic. stir in the vegetables and carrote with the chicken. Sizzle the wine then pour in the stock and seasoning. Blend in the cornflour mix and toss thoroughly. Dish and serve hot. Garnish with the carrot bird.

芝麻鸡
SESAME CHICKEN

材料：

鸡肉 250 克	芝麻 90 克
肥肉 300 克	芫荽叶作装饰
沸水 2 杯	炸油 4 杯
生粉 2 汤匙	

腌料：

姜汁 1 茶匙	胡椒粉 $^1/_4$ 茶匙
酒 1 茶匙	蛋白 $^1/_2$ 只
生粉 1 茶匙	

调味：

盐 $^1/_3$ 茶匙	麻油 1 茶匙
糖 $^1/_2$ 茶匙	

制法：

◆ 鸡肉洗净抹干剁成肉茸，加腌料和匀腌 10 分钟，拌入调味料挞匀。

◆ 肥肉置沸水中焓 10 分钟，冲冻后切成 3.75 × 5 公分薄片。

◆ 生粉涂匀在肥肉上，再将鸡茸铺在上面。鸡茸上洒满芝麻以手按紧，芫荽叶 1 片酿在上面装饰。

◆ 烧红锅，倒下炸油烧热。滑下鸡件，以文火炸至金黄色，排在碟中。花椒粉及喼汁跟上。

Ingredients:

250g chicken meat	90g sesame seeds
300g fat pork	parsley to garnish
2 cups boiling water	4 cups oil for deep frying
2 tbsp cornflour	

Marinade:

1 tsp ginger juice	$^1/_4$ tsp pepper
1 tsp wine	$^1/_2$ egg white
1 tsp cornflour	

Seasoning:

$^1/_3$ tsp salt	1 tsp sesame oil
$^1/_2$ tsp sugar	

Method:

◆ Wash and mince the chicken meat into a puree. Immerse in the marinade and set aside for 10 minutes. Blend in the seasoning and pound until springy.

◆ Cook the fat pork in the boiling water for 10 minutes. Refresh and slice into 3.75 cm × 5 cm thin pieces.

◆ Dust each piece of fat pork with a little cornflour then pile the chicken puree on top. Sprinkle the sesame seeds over the chicken then garnish with a parsley leaf. Press lightly to secure.

◆ Gently bring the oil to just boil. Deep fry the chicken until light brown. Remove and drain. Arrange on a platter to serve with xanthoxylum seed powder and Worcestershire sauce.

凉拌芝麻鸡

SHREDDED CHICKEN WITH ASSORTED VEGETABLES

材料:

鸡 1 只 1500 克　　马蹄 90 克
咸菜 90 克　　　　海蜇丝 125 克
红萝卜 90 克　　　木耳 8 克
青瓜 90 克　　　　炸核桃 1/4 杯
酸姜 90 克　　　　芝麻 1/4 杯

腌料:

姜汁 1 汤匙　　　　盐 1/2 汤匙
酒 1 汤匙

调味:

生抽 2 汤匙　　　　上汤 1/4 杯
糖 1 汤匙　　　　　胡椒粉 1/4 茶匙
麻酱 2 汤匙　　　　麻油 1 茶匙

制法:

◆ 鸡洗净抹干,以腌料擦匀内外腌 1/2 小时。放蒸笼内蒸 20 分钟,取出拆肉撕成鸡条。头翼留用。

◆ 咸菜切丝。红萝卜飞水与青瓜、酸姜同切丝。马蹄去皮洗净切丝。

◆ 海蜇丝用沸水略拖过,置水龙头下冲水 1 小时,捞起浸在冰水内 1 小时,取出以毛巾吸干水份,以麻油、生抽捞匀。

◆ 木耳浸透洗净剪去硬蒂。飞水后切丝以熟油捞匀。核桃剁碎,芝麻洗净烙香。

◆ 长碟一只将鸡头、翼砌回原形,鸡丝排放中央,四周围以杂菜丝。海蜇丝放在鸡丝上,将核桃、芝麻洒上置雪柜中 15 分钟。

◆ 调味料和匀试妥味淋在鸡上即成。

Ingredients:

1 chicken, about 1500g
90g preserved mustard cabbage
90g carrots
90g cucumber
90g pickled ginger
90g water chestnuts
125g shredded jelly fish
8g hard black fungus
1/4 cup toasted walnuts
1/4 cup sesame seeds

Marinade :

1 tbsp ginger juice　　1/2 tbsp salt
1 tbsp wine

Seasoning:

2 tbsp light soy　　　1/4 cup stock
1 tbsp sugar　　　　1/4 tsp pepper
2 tbsp sesame paste　1 tsp sesame oil

Method:

◆ Wash and dry the chicken. Soak it in the marinade for 30 minutes. Steam over medium heat for 20 minutes. Remove, debone and shred the chicken. Retain the chicken head and wings for later use.

◆ Shred the preserved mustard cabbage. Blanch and shred the carrots. Shred the cucumber and the pickled ginger. Peel, wash and shred the water chestnuts.

◆ Scald the jelly fish. Refresh under a running tap for 1 hour. Soak in iced water for another hour. Remove and towel dry. Mix evenly with some sesame oil and light soy.

◆ Soak, wash and trim the black fungua. Blanch and shred it, then mix it with a little oil. Chop the walnuts and parch the sesame seeds.

◆ Place the chicken head and wings along the edge of an oval platter to form the shape of a chicken. Put the shredded chicken in the centre and arrange the assorted vegetables around it. Scatter the jelly fish on the shredded chicken. Sprinkle the walnuts and sesame seeds on top and chill in the refrigerator for 15 minutes.

◆ Thoroughly mix the seanoning then pour the mixture over the chicken and vegetables. Serve cold.

双笋鸡柳

SHREDDED CHICKEN WITH BABY CORN

材料:

珍珠笋 90 克	姜 2 片
甘笋 90 克	葱头 2 粒
鸡肉 180 克	蒜头 2 粒
油 3 杯	芫荽 2 棵

腌料:

姜汁 2 茶匙	生粉 1 茶匙
酒 1 茶匙	

调味:

酒 1 茶匙	胡椒粉 1/4 茶匙
上汤 1/4 杯	生粉水 1 茶匙
生抽 1 茶匙	老抽 1/4 茶匙
蚝油 1 茶匙	麻油 1 茶匙
糖 1 茶匙	

制法:

◆ 珍珠笋、甘笋洗净切片。一同放于沸水中飞水，过冷河隔干水份。

◆ 鸡肉洗净切条，放入和匀腌料拌匀腌 30 分钟泡油。隔去余油。留下 1 汤匙油候用。

◆ 姜、葱、蒜头切丝。芫荽摘妥。

◆ 烧热锅中油，爆香姜、葱、蒜丝。倒入珍珠笋、甘笋及鸡条爆炒片刻。灒酒加上汤及调味料兜匀。随即以生粉水及老抽埋芡，最后洒麻油芫荽即可上桌。

Ingredients:

90g baby corn	3 cups warm oil
90g carrot	2 pieces ginger
2 cups boiling water	2 shallots
180g chicken breast	2 garlic cloves
	2 parsley sprigs

Marinade:

2 tsp ginger juice	1 tsp cornflour
1 tsp wine	

Seasoning:

1 tsp wine	1/4 tsp pepper
1/4 cup stock	1 tsp cornflour mix
1 tsp light soy	1/4 tsp dark soy
1 tsp oyster sauce	1 tsp sesame oil
1 tsp sugar	

Method:

◆ Wash and halve the baby corn. Peel and slice the carrot. Place both the vegetables in the boiling water to blanch for 1 minute. Refresh and drain.

◆ Clean, shred and immerse the chicken in the mixed marinade for 30 minutes. Parboil in the warm oil and drain. Leave 1 tbsp oil for later use.

◆ Shred the ginger, shallots and garlic. Trim the parsley.

◆ Heat the wok to bring the oil to the boil. Saute the ginger, shallots and garlic until pungent. Pour in the baby corn, carrot pieces and chicken to stir fry for 20 seconds. Sizzle the wine; add the stock and sesoning to mix well. Thicken the stock with the cornflour mix and dark soy. Stir in the sesame oil and parsley then dish.

鸡丝豆芽

SHREDDED CHICKEN WITH BEAN SPROUTS

材料：

鸡腿 250 克	姜 2 片
绿豆芽 250 克	蒜头 2 粒
西芹 60 克	油 3 汤匙
红椒 1 只	

腌料：

姜汁 1 汤匙	盐 $1/4$ 茶匙
酒 1 汤匙	水 2 汤匙
生粉 1 茶匙	油 1 汤匙（后下）

调味：

盐 $1/8$ 茶匙	生抽 2 茶匙
酒 1 茶匙	糖 $1/2$ 茶匙
上汤 2 汤匙	

制法：

◆ 鸡腿去骨去皮切丝用腌鸡料和匀腌 $1/2$ 小时，加油 1 汤匙和匀再腌 1 小时。

◆ 绿豆芽摘去尾洗净隔干水份，西芹撕去硬脉切 3.75 公分丝。红椒去籽切丝。姜切丝，蒜头切片。

◆ 烧红锅加油 $1 1/2$ 汤匙煮沸爆香一半姜蒜。倾入鸡丝拌炒 1 分钟，铲起候用。

◆ 另锅烧红加油 $1 1/2$ 汤匙爆香一半姜蒜。倒下豆芽、西芹快速兜炒约 8 下，即加红椒丝及鸡丝拌匀。灒酒加调味猛火炒匀，即可上碟。

Ingredients :

250g chicken thighs	1 red chilli
250g bean sprouts	2 slices ginger
60g celery	2 garlic cloves
	3 tbsp oil

Marinade:

1 tbsp ginger juice	2 tbsp water
1 tbsp wine	1 tbsp oil (to be added last)
1 tsp cornflour	
$1/4$ tsp salt	

Seasoning:

$1/8$ tsp salt	2 tsp light soy
1 tsp wine	$1/2$ tsp sugar
2 tbsp stock	

Method:

◆ Debone, remove the skin and shred the chicken thighs. Immerse in the mixed marinade for 30 minutes then add the oil and set aside for l hour.

◆ Trim, wash and drain the bean sprouts. Shred the celery into 3.75 cm sections. Deseed and shred the chilli and the ginger. Slice the garlic .

◆ Heat a wok and bring half the oil to the boil. Saute half of the ginger and garlic. Pour in the chicken to stir fry for 1 minutn. Remove.

◆ Heat another wok with the remaining oil to saute the rest of the ginger and garlic. Add the bean sprouts and celery to fry for about 8 seconds. Put in the chilli and the chicken to mix well. Sizzle the wine and trickle in the mixed seasoning to toss thoroughly. Dish ande srve.

西芹鸡柳

SHREDDED CHICKEN WITH CELERY

材料：

鸡胸肉 300 克   蒜头 2 粒
西芹 180 克   葱 2 棵
红萝卜 60 克   油 2 汤匙
姜 2 片

腌料：

姜汁 1 茶匙   糖 $^1/_2$ 茶匙
酒 1 汤匙   生粉 1 茶匙
盐 $^1/_8$ 茶匙   油 1 汤匙

调味：

盐 $^1/_4$ 茶匙   糖 $^3/_4$ 茶匙
酒 1 茶匙   胡椒粉 $^1/_4$ 茶匙
上汤 $^1/_4$ 杯   生粉水 1 茶匙
生抽 1 茶匙

制法：

◆ 鸡胸洗净去皮切粗条，放入腌料中腌 10 分钟。
◆ 西芹撕去筋，红萝卜去皮同洗净切粗条，飞水冲冻。
◆ 姜切丝、蒜头切片，葱洗净切度。
◆ 烧红锅，将油倒入，洒盐爆香姜、蒜头。加入鸡柳、西芹及红萝卜炒数下。潎酒加上汤及调味料和匀，拌入葱度上碟

Ingredients:

300g chicken breast   2 slices ginger
180g celery   2 cloves garlic
60g carrot   2 spring onions
     2 tbsp oil

Marinade:

1 tsp ginger juice $^1/_2$ tsp sugar
1tbsp wine   1 tsp cornflour
$^1/_8$ tsp salt   1 tbsp oil

Seasoning:

$^1/_4$ tsp salt $^3/_4$ tsp sugar
1 tsp wine $^1/_4$ tsp pepper
$^1/_4$ cup stock $^1/_2$ tsp cornflour
1 tsp light soy $^1/_2$ tsp water

Method:

◆ Shred the chicken into thick strips. Immerse in the marinade for 10 minutes.
◆ Shred the celery and carrot; blanch in boiling water then refresh. Shred the ginger; slice the garlic and section the spring onions.
◆ Heat a wok and sprinkle in the salt. Saute the ginger and garlic until aromatic. Add the chicken, celery and carrot and stir fry briefly. Sizzle the wine; trickle in the stock and seasoning and thicken into a gravy. Dish with the spring onions scattered on top.

季豆鸡丝

SHREDDED CHICKEN WITH FRENCH BEAN

材料：

鸡胸肉 180 克	葱头 1 粒
季豆 375 克	蒜头 1 粒
姜 2 片	

腌料：

姜汁 1 汤匙	蛋白 1 只
酒 1 茶匙	盐 $1/4$ 茶匙
生粉 1 茶匙	

调味：

盐 $1/2$ 茶匙	胡椒粉 $1/4$ 茶匙
酒 1 茶匙	生粉水 1 茶匙
上汤 $1/2$ 杯	麻油 1 茶匙
糖 1 茶匙	

制法：

◆ 鸡胸肉洗净切长幼丝，放入和匀之腌料中腌 $1/2$ 小时，泡嫩油后捞起，留下油2汤匙候用。

◆ 季豆撕去硬脉斜切成3.75公分度，姜切丝，葱蒜头切片。

◆ 烧红锅加油1汤匙煮沸爆香一半姜葱蒜，倾入季豆洒盐快速拌炒，边炒边洒上汤少许。豆软时马上盛起。

◆ 再烧红锅加油 1 汤匙爆香其余一半姜葱蒜，潵酒倾入上汤及调味料加生粉水和成芡，将鸡丝倒回锅中拌匀淋在季豆上即成。

Ingredients:

180g chicken breast	2 slices ginger
3 cups oil	1 shallot
375g French bean	1 garlic clove

Marinade :

1 tbsp ginger juice	1 egg white
1 tsp wine	$1/4$ tsp salt
1 tsp cornflour	

Seasoning:

$1/2$ tsp salt	$1/4$ tsp pepper
1 tsp wine	1 tsp cornflour mix
$1/4$ cups skock	1 tsp sesame oil
1 tsp sugar	

Method:

◆ Clean the chicken breast and shred into long and thin strips. Immerse in the marinade and set aside for 30 minutes. Parboil in the warm oil and drain; retain 2 tbsp oil for later use.

◆ Trim and cut the French beans lengthwise into 3.75 cm segments. Shred the ginger finely. Slice the shallot and garlic.

◆ Heat a wok with l tbsp oil to saute half of the ginger. shallot and garlic until pungent. Pour in the beans to fry briskly. Sprinkle in the salt and 2 tbsp stock to stir until evenly mixed. Remove on to a platter.

◆ Reheat the wok to bring the remaining oil to boil. Saute the other half of the ginger, shallot and garlic. Sizzle in the wine, pour in the stock and thicken with the cornflour mix. Return the shredded chicken into the wok to mix thoroughly then scoop over the beans and serve hot.

蚝油手撕鸡

SHREDDED CHICKEN WITH OYSTER SAUCE

材料：

鸡腿 2 只共约 500 克　　　脆花生 30 克
大菜丝 15 克　　　　　　　葱 2 棵

腌鸡料：

姜汁 2 汤匙　　　　　　　盐 $^1/_3$ 茶匙
酒 2 汤匙　　　　　　　　糖 1 茶匙

调味：

上汤 $^1/_4$ 杯　　　　　　　胡椒粉 $^1/_4$ 茶匙
蚝油 3 汤匙　　　　　　　麻油 1 茶匙
糖 1 茶匙

制法：

◆ 鸡腿以沸水洗净。每边斜切三刀，放在碟上。
◆ 腌鸡料放在小碗内拌匀，先淋一半在鸡腿之一边。反转鸡腿，将其余一半腌料平均倒下放置一旁腌 1 小时。中途将鸡腿转身 2 次腌 1 小时。中途将鸡腿转身 2 次使入味。置蒸笼内蒸 12 分钟，取出晾凉撕成鸡条，粗幼与大菜相等。
◆ 大菜丝用温水洗净，剪为 5 公分小段，排放在平碟上，再将鸡条铺在上面。
◆ 脆花生椿碎，葱洗净切粒。
◆ 小锅一个洗净，将调味料和匀倾入文火煮沸。试妥味后淋在鸡肉上。再洒花生碎及葱粒铺面。即可上桌。

Ingredients:

2 chicken thighs about 500g　　30g toasted peanuts
15g agar agar　　　　　　　　2 spring onione

Chicken Marinade:

2 tbsp ginger juice　　　$^1/_3$ tap salt
2 tbsp wine　　　　　　1 tep sugar

seasoning :

$^1/_4$ cup stock　　　　　　$^1/_4$ tsp pepper
3 tbsp oyster sauce　　　1 tsp sesame oil
1 tsp sugar

Method:

◆ Rinse the chicken thighs with boiling water and pat dry with a clean towel. Slash 3 slits lengthwise on each side and place on to a platter.
◆ Mix the marinade thoroughly in a small bowl. Pour half of the marinade on to one side of the chicken thighs and turn over the other side to coat with the remaining marinade. Set aside for an hour. Turn the thighs over every 20 minutes. Place in a steamer to cook for 12 minutes. Remove and set aside to cool. Tear the flesh into thick strips of similar size to the agar agar.
◆ Wash the agar agar in warm water and towel dry. Cut into 5 cm lenghts and arrange on a platter. Top with the chicken shreds.
◆ Crush the peanuts. Wash and dice the spring onions.
◆ Clean a small saucepan and pour in the mixed seasoning to bring to the boil. Season to taste and scoop on to the chicken. Sprinkle with the crushed peanuts and spring onions and serve cold.

红椰菜鸡丝

SHREDDED CHICKEN WITH RED CABBAGE

材料：

鸡胸肉 150 克 蒜头 1 粒
红椰菜 300 克 葱 2 棵
姜 2 片 油 3 汤匙

腌鸡料：

姜汁 1 茶匙 生粉 1 茶匙
酒 1 茶匙 水 1 汤匙
盐 1/8 茶匙 麻油 1 茶匙（后下）
糖 1/4 茶匙

调味：

盐 1/4 茶匙 生抽 1 茶匙
上汤 2 汤匙 糖 1/2 茶匙

制法：

◆ 鸡胸肉切 3.75 公分 × 0.6 公分粗条，放在和匀之腌料中拌妥置一旁 1/2 小时。加入麻油搅匀再腌 1/2 小时。

◆ 红椰菜洗净切粗条。姜切丝，蒜头切片，葱切度。全部配料放在碟上候用。

◆ 煎锅或锅洗净烧热，将一半油倾入爆香姜丝，随即把鸡丝放入炒匀至肉变白色，即可盛起。

◆ 另锅烧热将其余一半油倒下煮沸，滑下蒜片爆香即将椰菜倾入洒盐炒片刻。加入鸡丝拌炒数下，将上汤边炒边洒入，再将其余调味料放入兜匀。试妥味，洒葱度搅匀上碟。

Ingredients:

150g chicken fillet 2 slices ginger
300g red cabbage 1 garlic clove
  2 spring onions
  3 tbsp oil

Chicken Marinade:

1 tsp ginger juice 1 tsp cornflour
1 tsp wine 1 tbsp water
1/8 tsp salt 1 tsp sesame oil, to be
1/4 tsp sugar added last

Seasoning:

1/4 tsp salt 1 tsp light soy
2 tbsp stock 1/2 tsp sugar

Method:

◆ Shred the chicken fillet into 4 cm x 0.6 cm strips and put into the above marinade cexcept the sesame oil to stand for 30 minutes. Blend in the sesame oil and set aside for a further 30 minutes.

◆ Wash and slice the red cabbage. Shred the ginger. Slice the garlic. Section the spring onions. Put all these ingredients on a platter for later use.

◆ Heat a pan or wok to bring half the oil to the boil. Saute the ginger and stir in the chicken to fry until the chicken meat turns white. Remove and drain.

◆ Heat another wok and bring the remaining oil to the boil. Slide in the garlic to saute until fragrant. Pour in the red cabbage and salt to stir fry for 2 minutes then add the shredded chicken to toss well. Sprinkle in the stock gradually to mix thoroughly. Season to taste. Scatter the spring onions on top and dish.

龙穿凤翼

SHREDDED HAM IN CHICKEN WINGS

材料:

酒 1 汤匙　　　　　火腿丝 20 条
水 3 杯　　　　　　油 3 汤匙
姜 2 片　　　　　　菜软 250 克
鸡翼 20 只　　　　沸水 1 杯
红萝卜丝或　　　　盐 1 茶匙
西芹丝 20 条　　　火腿茸 1 汤匙

调味:

酒 1 茶匙　　　　　生抽 1 茶匙
上汤 1/2 杯　　　　胡椒粉 1/4 茶匙
盐 1/2 茶匙　　　　麻油 1/2 茶匙
糖 1 茶匙

芡料:

生粉 1 茶匙　　　　老抽 1/4 茶匙
水 1 汤匙　　　　　麻油 1 茶匙

制法:

◆ 烧红锅, 灒酒加入水及姜片煮沸。将鸡翼放入飞水 5 至 6 分钟, 捞起置水龙头下冲净脂肪, 取出隔干水份后斩去头尾 2 度, 只余中段。

◆ 将中段鸡翼内之两条骨取出, 酿入红萝卜丝及火腿丝, 排放在碟上。

◆ 再烧红锅加入油 1 汤匙煮沸, 灒酒 1/2 茶匙加上汤及调味料重煮沸, 淋在酿妥之鸡翼上。放入蒸笼内蒸 10 分钟后取出, 蒸鸡上汤留起候用。

◆ 菜软放于沸水中加余油及盐 1 茶匙飞水, 捞起隔去水份, 围放在碟边。

◆ 另锅烧热, 灒下余酒加蒸鸡上汤。调妥味后以生粉水埋芡, 淋在鸡翼上, 以火腿茸洒面上桌即成。

Ingredients:

1 tbsp wine
3 cups water
2 slices ginger
20 chicken wings
20 shredded carrots or celery
20 shredded Virginia ham
3 tbsp corn oil
250g green vegetables
1 cup boiling water
1 tsp salt
1 tbsp chopped ham

Seasoning:

1 tsp wine
1/2 cup stock
1/2 tsp salt
1 tsp sugar
1 tsp light soy
1/4 tsp pepper
1/2 tsp sesame oil

Gravy Mix:

1 tsp cornflour
1 tbsp water
1/4 tsp dark soy
1 tsp sesame oil

Method:

◆ Heat a wok, sizzle the wine and pour in the water with the ginger to bring to the boil. Add the chicken wings to blanch for 5 to 6 minutes. Refresh under a running tap and drain. Cut away both ends of the wings and retain the middle section.

◆ Remove the bones from the wings and fill each hole with a piece of ham and carrot. Arrange on to a platter.

◆ Reheat the wok and bring 1 tbsp of oil to boil. Sprinkle in half of the wine and add the stock and seasoning. Pour over the wings and steam for 10 minutes. Remove and retain the stock for later use.

◆ Blanch the vegetables in the boiling water with the remaining oil and the salt. Remove and drain. Arrange round the edge of the platter.

◆ Heat another wok, sizzle the remaining wine and pour in the stock from the steamed chicken. Season to taste. Thicken the sauce with the gravy mix. Scoop over the chicke wings then scatter the chopped ham on top and serve.

茶香熏鸡腿
SMOKED CHICKEN THIGHS

材料:

鸡腿 4 只约 1000 克　　　茶叶 1/3 杯
油 3 杯　　　　　　　　　沙糖 1/3 杯
　　　　　　　　　　　　麻油 1 茶匙

调味:

老抽 3 汤匙　　　　　　　葱头茸 1/2 汤匙
糖 2 汤匙　　　　　　　　生粉 1/2 茶匙
姜茸 1/2 汤匙　　　　　　胡椒粉 1/4 茶匙

制法:

◆ 鸡腿洗净以刀略拍后，割开取出骨头。将鸡肉摊开以刀背拍松。
◆ 盆中放姜汁、酒各 3 汤匙，将鸡腿肉放入腌 20 分钟。倒入已混和之调味料拌匀再腌 1 小时，中途转身一次。
◆ 锅中放油 3 杯煮至仅沸，将鸡腿肉放入炸片刻，捞起隔净余油。
◆ 另锅放锡纸一张，将茶叶倒入。中火烧热洒下沙糖至起烟时，放一涂油铁架在锅中把鸡腿排放在架上。盖上锅盖熏 5 分钟。反转再熏 5 分钟至金黄色即可。取出涂上麻油切细件上碟。

Ingredients:

4 chicken thighs, about 1000g　　1/3 cup tea leaf
3 cups oil　　　　　　　　　　1/3 cup sugar
　　　　　　　　　　　　　　1 tsp sesame oil

Seasoning:

3 tbsp dark soy　　　　　1/2 tbsp minced shallot
2 tbsp sugar　　　　　　1/2 tsp cornflour
1/2 tbsp minced ginger　　1/4 tsp pepper

Method:

◆ Wash and debone the chicken thighs. Place the chicken on the table with the skin facing downwards. Pound with the back of the cleaver.
◆ Pour 3 tbsp each of ginger juice and wine into the mixing bowl. Put in the chicken meat to marinate for 20 minutes. Mix in the seasoning to marinate the chicken for an hour. Turn the chicken occasionally.
◆ Bring the oil to the boil in a wok. Deep fry the chicken for 1 to 2 minutes. Remove and drain.
◆ Line a piece of foil on a heated wok. Pour in the tea leaves to heat for a few seconds. Add the sugar to heat until white smoke appears. Place a greased rack in the wok and lay the chicken onto it. Cover and smoke for 5 minutes. Turn and smoke the other side until both sides are golden. Remove and grease with sesame oil. Cut and serve.

玫瑰油鸡
SOY SAUCE CHICKEN

材料：

鸡 1 只重 1500 克	卤水 4 杯
粗盐 2 汤匙	老抽 3 杯
水 1/2 锅	糖 1 杯
姜 3 片	玫瑰露 2 汤匙
葱 3 棵	麻油 1 汤匙

制法：

◆ 鸡去内脏洗净以盐擦匀鸡身内外，再冲洗干净。

◆ 水烧沸将鸡淋至收缩后吊干。姜拍扁，葱摘妥洗净候用。

◆ 卤水、老抽与姜、糖同注入锅中以中火烧沸后，将鸡放入待重沸时，即可熄火加入玫瑰露及葱。盖锅盖浸 15 分钟，揭盖将鸡翻身再煮沸，熄火盖密再浸 13 分钟。

◆ 将鸡取出待凉涂以麻油，斩件排成鸡形，即可上桌。

Ingredients:

1 chicken, about 1500g	4 cups spicy sauce
2 tbsp coarse salt	8 cups dark soy
1/2 wok water	1 cup sugar
3 slices ginger	2 tbsp rose wine
3 spring onions	1 tbsp sesame oil

Method:

◆ Rub the salt inside the chicken and rinse thoroughly. Pour boiling water over the chicken to tighten the skin. Mash the ginger and trim the spring onions.

◆ Place the spicy sauce, dark soy, ginger and sugar into the saucepan and bring to the boil. Put the chicken into the saucepan, reboil and turn off the heat. Add the rose wine and spring onions. Set aside and soak for 15 minutes. Turn over the chicken and return the sauce to the boil. Turn off the heat again and set aside for another 13 minutes.

◆ Remove the chicken and leave to cool, then rub it with the sesame oil, chop into serving pieces and dish.

南瓜童鸡

SPICY CHICKEN IN PUMPKIN

材料：

南瓜 1 个约重 2000 克	葱 2 棵
童鸡 1000 克	五香炒米粉 60 克
姜 2 片	油 4 杯作泡油用

调味：

盐 1/2 茶匙	绍酒 1 汤匙
糖 2 汤匙	南乳 1 汤匙
鸡粉 1/4 茶匙	老抽 1/2 汤匙

制法：

◆ 南瓜依皮上凹凸纹切开顶部使成盖子（看图）。将瓜子全部挖去，瓜身当作炖盅。

◆ 鸡洗擦干净以毛巾吸干水份，斩成大件候用。

◆ 姜片及葱剁茸，与上述调味料及五香米粉捞匀，将鸡件放入腌 20 分钟。

◆ 烧红锅加入油煮至微温时，即将鸡件放入泡油 2 分钟。取出隔净余油。

◆ 将隔净油之鸡件转盛在南瓜内，盖上瓜盖。放入蒸笼内蒸 40 分钟。取出上桌，甘香浓郁，可酒可饭。

Ingredients:

1 pumpkin, about 2000g	2 spring onions
1000g spring chicken	60g spicy rice flour
2 slices ginger	4 cups oil for parboiling

Seasoning:

1/2 tsp salt	1 tbsp fermented red beancurd
2 tbsp sugar	
1/4 tsp chicken powder	1/2 tbsp dark soy
1 tbsp yellow wine	

Method:

◆ Cut and carve the pumpkin to form a pot with a lid (Refer to photograph). Remove all the seeds.

◆ Wash, clean and dry the chicken. Chop into serving pieces.

◆ Mince the ginger and spring onions to mix well with the seasoning and rice flour. Put the chicken into the mixed seasoning and marinate for 20 minutes.

◆ Heat a wok and add the oil to cook until warm. Pour in the chicken to parboil for 2 minutes. Remove and drain.

◆ Transfer the chicken into the pumpkin and cover with the lid. Place in the steamer and cook over high heat for 40 minutes. Remove on to a platter and serve hot.

腊肠蒸鸡

STEAMED CHICKEN WITH SAUSAGES

材料:

鸡脾或胸肉 300 克	腊肠或香肠 2 条
姜丝 1 汤匙	葱丝 1 汤匙
白菌 60 克	

腌鸡料:

姜汁 1 茶匙	酒 1 茶匙

调味:

盐 1/4 茶匙	胡椒粉 1/4 茶匙
糖 1 1/2 茶匙	生粉 1 茶匙
蚝油 1 汤匙	水 1 汤匙
生抽 1 汤匙	麻油 1 茶匙

制法:

◆ 鸡胸肉洗净去骨切件,以上述腌料和匀腌20分钟。

◆ 白菌洗净修妥切厚片。腊肠洗净切片。

◆ 将鸡肉、白菌片、腊肠片一同放在深碟中,拌入额外清水1茶匙及油1汤匙捞匀。置蒸笼内以中火蒸12分钟。取出洒下姜丝及葱丝。上桌熟食。

Ingredients:

300g chicken thigh or breast	1 tbsp shredded ginger
60g fresh mushrooms	1 tbsp shredded spring onions
2 Chinese sausages or pork sausages	

Chicken Marinade:

1 tsp ginger juice	1 tsp wine

Seasoning:

1/4 tsp salt	1/4 tsp pepper
1 1/2 tsp sugar	4 tsp cornflour
1 tbsp oyster sauce	1 tbap water
1 tbsp soy sauce	1 tsp sesame oil

Method:

◆ Clean debone and cut the chicken into bite- sized piecee. Mix in the above marinade and set aside for 20 minutes. Blend in all the seasoning to marinate for another 20 minutes.

◆ Wash, trim and slice the mushrooms. Wash and slice the sausages.

◆ Place the marinated chicken, mushrooms and sausages on a platter. Add an extra tsp of water and 1 tbsp of oil to mix well. Arrange in a steamer to cook for 12 minutes over moderate heat. Remove and sprinkle the shredded ginger and spring onions on top. Serve hot.

蚝油焗鸡

STEWED CHICKEN IN OYSTER SAUCE

材料：

鸡腿 600 克	葱头 2 粒
老抽 2 汤匙	蒜头 2 粒
熟冬菇 10 只	芫荽 3 棵
红萝卜 125 克	炸油 3 杯
姜 3 片	

调味：

酒 2 茶匙	蚝油 2 汤匙
上汤 1 杯	糖 1 茶匙
生抽 1 茶匙	胡椒粉 $1/8$ 茶匙

芡料：

生粉 1 茶匙	老抽 $1/2$ 茶匙
水 1 汤匙	

制法：

◆ 鸡腿洗净抹干，用老抽涂在鸡上。

◆ 冬菇斜刀片开，红萝卜飞水切片，姜、葱、蒜头剁茸，芫荽摘妥。

◆ 烧红锅倒下炸油煮沸，将鸡放入炸至浅黄时捞起，盛起隔清余油，留起油 1 汤匙作起锅用。

◆ 锅中余油烧热投入姜片、葱头、蒜头、红萝卜、冬菇，溅下酒，即加上汤及调味品，同时将鸡放入。盖上锅盖，焗五分钟。取出斩件，余汁加芡料煮浓，淋在鸡件上，以芫荽装饰。

Ingredients:

600g chicken thighs	3 slices ginger
2 tbsp dark soy	2 shallots
10 cooked Chinese mushroome	2 garlic cloves
125g carrot	3 parsley sprigs
	3 cups oil for deep frying

Seasoning:

2 tsp sherry	2 tbsp oyster sauce
1 cup stock	1 tsp sugar
1 tsp light soy	$1/8$ tsp pepper

Gravy Mix:

1 tsp cornflour	$1/2$ tsp dark soy
1 tbsp water	

Method:

◆ Clean and dry the chicken with a towel. Brush evenly with the dark soy.

◆ Slice the mushrooms. Blanch and slice the carrot. Mince the ginger, shallots and garlic. Trim the parsley.

◆ Bring the oil to boil in a heated wok to deep fry the chicken until golden brown. Drain and leave 1 tbsp of oil in the wok.

◆ Reheat the oil in the wok to saute the ginger, shallots and garlic. Sizzle the sherry then pour in the stock and seasoning. Return the chicken into the wok. Add the mushrooms and carrot to simmer for 5 minutes. Remove the chicken on to a chopping board and cut into bite-sized pieces. Arrange on a platter with the mushrooms and carrot. Thicken the sauce with the gravy mix. Pour over tbe chicken and serve hot. Garnish with the parsley.

蜜糖子姜鸡
STEWED CHICKEN WITH GTNGER AND HONEY

材料：

嫩鸡 500 克
子姜 150 克
盐 1 茶匙
葱头 4 粒

蒜头 4 粒
红椒 2 只
葱 2 棵
油 1 汤匙

腌料：

姜汁 2 汤匙
酒 2 汤匙

生抽 1 茶匙
生粉 1 汤匙

调味：

酒 1 茶匙
上汤 1 杯
生抽 2 汤匙

胡椒粉 $1/4$ 茶匙
蜜糖 2 汤匙

制法：

◆ 鸡斩件后和匀腌料腌 30 分钟后泡油候用。
◆ 子姜切件以盐略腌后洗净，放于白锅中烙干。
◆ 葱、蒜头拍扁，红椒切件，葱切度。
◆ 烧红锅加油 1 汤匙爆香葱、蒜头，将鸡倾入加子姜迅速炒片刻。潜酒倒入上汤及调味料拌匀炆 5 分钟。揭盖将红椒及葱度加入抛匀上碟。

Ingredients:

500g chicken
150g young
ginger shoots
1 tsp salt
4 shallots

4 garlic cloves
2 red chillies
2 spring onions
1 tbsp oil

Marinade:

2 tbsp ginger juice
2 tbsp wine

1 tsp light soy
1 tbsp cornflour

Seasoning:

1 tsp wine
1 cup stock
2 tbsp light soy

$1/4$ tsp pepper
2 tbsp honey

Method:

◆ Chop the chicken into large pieces. Tmmerse in the marinade for 20 minutes then set aside for 20 minutes. Parboil and drain.
◆ Out the ginger shoots into thick pieces and coat with salt. set aside for 20 minutes then refresh and dry. Put the ginger shoots in a heated wok and parch thoroughly.
◆ Mash the shallot and garlic; deseed and wedge the red chillies; section the spring onions.
◆ Reheat the wok with oil and saute the shallot and garlic until aromatic. Drop in the chicken and ginger and stir fry for 2 minutes. Sizzle the wine, trickle in the stock and seasoning. Cover and simmer for 5 minutes. Mix in the chillies and spring onions and serve.

冬菇炆鸡

STEWED CHICKEN WITH MUSHROOMS

材料：

鸡腿 375 克	葱头 3 粒
姜汁 1 汤匙	蒜头 2 粒
酒 1 汤匙	熟冬菇 180 克
水 3 汤匙	葱度 2 汤匙
生粉 1/2 汤匙	洋葱花装饰
姜 3 片	

调味：

酒 1 茶匙	蚝油 1 汤匙
鸡上汤 1 杯	糖 1/2 汤匙
盐 1/4 茶匙	胡椒粉 1/4 茶匙
生抽 1 汤匙	麻油 1 茶匙

制法：

◆ 鸡腿洗净去皮去骨切大件以姜汁、酒及水和匀腌 1 小时，加入生粉拌匀续腌 1 小时。

◆ 姜、葱头、蒜头全部去皮切片。

◆ 烧红锅，加油 1 汤匙煮沸。放入姜、葱、蒜爆香，将鸡肉倒下炒匀。潜酒倾入鸡上汤及冬菇，盖上锅盖文火炆 5 分钟，加入调味料续炆 5 分钟。至只余少许水份时，滴下麻油，拌入葱度盛起上桌。以洋葱花装饰。

Ingredients:

375g chicken thighs	3 shallots
1 tbsp ginger juice	2 garlic cloves
1 tbsp wine	180g cooked mushrooms
3 tbsp water	2 tbsp sectioned spring onions
1/2 tbsp cornflour	onion flower to garnish
3 slices ginger	

Seasoning:

1 tsp wine	1 tbsp oyster sauce
1 cup chicken stock	1/2 tbsp sugar
1/4 tsp salt	1/4 tsp pepper
1 tbsp light soy	1 tsp sesame oil

Method:

◆ Wash the chicken thighs and remove the skin. Debone, cut into serving pieces and immerse in the ginger juice, wine and water to marinate for 1 hour. Stir in the cornflour to mix well and set aside for another hour.

◆ Peel and slice the ginger, shallots and garlic.

◆ Heat a wok and bring 1 tbsp oil to boil. Saute the ginger, shallots and garlic till pungent. Slide in the chicken to fry for 3 minutes. Sizzle the wine, pour in the stock and mushrooms. Cover and simmer for 5 minutes. Add the seasoning and continue to stew for 5 minutes until there is only about 1/4 cup sauce left. Sprinkle the sesame oil and spring onions on top and dish. Garnish with the onion flower.

仙掌鱼唇

STEWED DUCK'S WEBS WITH FISH MAW

材料：

雪藏鱼唇 250 克	沸油 4 杯
沸水 8 杯	八角 3 粒
姜 3 片	花椒 ½ 茶匙
酒 1 汤匙	陈皮 1 方英寸
鸭脚 16 只	桂皮 1 方英寸
老抽 2 汤匙	葱头 2 片
葱 2 棵（切度）	

调味：

盐 ½ 茶匙	蚝油 1 茶匙
酒 1 汤匙	糖 ½ 茶匙
生抽 1 茶匙	胡椒粉 ¼ 茶匙

芡料：

生粉 1 茶匙	麻油 1 茶匙
水 1 汤匙	

制法：

◆ 鱼唇解冻后放于 3 杯沸水中飞水 2 分钟，取出切 5 公分段。放入另 3 杯沸水中加姜 2 片及酒再飞水，捞起过冷河抹干水份。姜弃去，沸水留起候用。

◆ 鸭脚擦净剪去趾甲，放入以上沸水中飞水 3 分钟，取出冲净后以老抽涂匀。随即放入沸油中炸至金黄色，捞起过冷河隔干水份。锅中留下 1 汤匙油候用。

◆ 另 2 杯沸水放入瓦锅中，加入各香料、姜 1 片及鸭脚。以中火炆 1 至 2 小时，挟起置碟中央，汁留用。

◆ 烧热锅中余油，爆香葱片。灒酒倒下鸭汁 1 杯，加鸭脚、鱼唇及调味料。盖上锅盖煮 10 分钟，揭盖以生粉水埋芡。再滴下麻油及洒葱度即可上碟。

Ingrediens:

250g frozen fish maw	½ tsp xanthoxylum seeds
8 cups boiling water	1 sq. in. (2.5 cm) tangerine peel
3 slices ginger	1 sq. in. (2.5 cm) cinnamon bark
1 tbsp wine	
16 duck's webs	2 sliced shallots
2 tbsp dark soy	2 sectioned chives
4 cups hot oil	
3 star anises	

Seasoning:

½ tsp salt	1 tsp oyster sauce
1 tbsp sherry	½ tsp sugar
1 tsp light soy	¼ tsp pepper

Gravy Mix:

1 tsp cornflour	1 tsp sesame oil
1 tbsp water	

Method:

◆ Defrost and blanch the fish maw in 3 cups of the boiling water for 2 minutes. Remove and cut into 5 cm sections then blanch in another 3 cups of the boiling water with 2 slices of the above ginger and the wine. Refresh and dry. Discard the ginger and keep the liquid.

◆ Clean and remove all the nails from the duck's webs. Blanch in the above boiling water for 3 minutes. Remove and rinse, brush with the dark soy. Deep fry in the boiling oil until golden brown. Remove, refresh and drain. Keep 1 tbsp oil for sauteeing.

◆ Bring the last 2 cups of water to boil in a saucepan. Put in the spices, remaining slice of ginger and the duck's webs. Simmer over moderate heat for 1 to 2 hours. Remove and keep the juice to use as stock.

◆ Heat the wok to bring the remaining oil to boil. Saute the shallote until fragrant. Sizzle the wine and pour in 1 cup of the duck juice. Return the duck's webs and fish maw into the wok with the seasoning. Cover and simmer for 10 minutes. Remove the lid and thicken the sauce with the gravy mix. Add the sesame oil and scatter the chives on top. Dish and serve.

江南百花鸡
STUFFED CHICKEN WITH PRAWN PUREE

材料:

鸡皮1只　　　　　　红萝卜花6片
（可连肉少许）　　芫荽2棵
虾肉500克　　　　　菜软180克
马蹄60克　　　　　油1汤匙
生粉1汤匙

腌料:

盐 $^3/_4$ 茶匙　　　　生粉2茶匙
糖 $^1/_4$ 茶匙　　　　蛋白 $^1/_2$ 只
胡椒粉 $^1/_4$ 茶匙

调味:

酒1茶匙　　　　　麻油1茶匙
上汤 $^3/_4$ 杯　　　　蛋白1只
生粉水2茶匙

制法:

◆ 鸡皮连肉洗净以毛巾抹干，虾肉去肠洗净抹干吹至干透压成虾泥。

◆ 马蹄去皮切幼，加入虾泥中拌匀。拌入腌料搞匀挞至起胶有弹性，再置冰箱中雪1小时。

◆ 鸡皮平放在桌上，洒下生粉，酿入虾胶按平。以红萝卜花及芫荽贴在虾肉上装饰，放碟上置蒸笼内以猛火蒸8分钟取出，切件排在另一只热碟上。

◆ 菜软洗净加一半油炒熟，围在碟边。

◆ 烧热锅加入余油煮沸，潲酒倾入上汤，调妥味后，以生粉水和成芡，拌入蛋白麻油搞匀淋在鸡上。

Ingredients:

1 whole chicken skin	6 slices carrot
500g shelled	2 parsley sprigs
prawns	180g green
60g water	vegetables
chestnuts	1 tsp oil
1 tbsp cornflour	

Prawn Marinade:

$^3/_4$ tsp salt	2 tsp cornflour
$^1/_4$ tsp sugar	$^1/_2$ egg white
$^1/_4$ tsp pepper	

Seasoning:

1 tsp wine	1 tsp sesame oil
$^3/_4$ cup stock	1 egg white
2 tsp cornflour mix	

Method:

◆ Clean and towel dry the chicken skin. Devein, wash, towel dry and mash the prawns into a puree.

◆ Dice the water chestnuts finely and mix with the prawn puree. Blend in the marinade to mix thoroughly then pound until firm and springy. Chill in the refrigerator for 1 hour.

◆ Lay the chicken, with skin facing downwards, on the table and sprinkle the cornflour over it. Spread the puree evenly on the skin and press slightly to smooth the surface. Garnish with the carrot and parsley leaves. Place on a platter to steam over high heat for 8 minutes and remove. Chop into serving pieces and arrange on another hot platter.

◆ Wash and stir fry the vegetables with half of the oil then arrange round the chicken.

◆ Reheat the wok and bring the remaining oil to the boil. Sizzle the wine, add the stock and season to taste. Thicken the sauce with the cornflour mix and stir in the beaten egg white and sesame oil. Mask over the stuffed chicken and serve.

川椒仙掌

DUCK'S WEB IN HOT SAUCE

材料：

去骨鸭掌 180 克	红椒 30 克
水 2 杯	青椒 60 克
姜 4 片	珍珠笋 90 克
葱头 2 粒	蒜头 2 粒
油 2 汤匙	

腌料：

酒 1 汤匙	糖 1 茶匙
姜汁 1 汤匙	胡椒粉 $^1/_4$ 茶匙
生抽 1 茶匙	

调味：

盐 $^1/_4$ 茶匙	生抽 1 茶匙
豆瓣酱 1 汤匙	糖 1 茶匙
酒 1 茶匙	生粉水 1 茶匙
上汤 $^1/_4$ 杯	

制法：

◆ 鸭掌用和匀腌料腌 $^1/_2$ 小时后，置沸水中加一半姜及葱头煮 10 分钟，洗净抹干。青红椒去籽切件，珍珠笋围边，其余一半姜葱及蒜头剁茸。

◆ 烧红锅，加油煮沸，洒盐爆香姜、葱、蒜。倾入鸭掌拌炒 5 分钟，即加豆瓣酱及青红椒、珍珠笋拌炒。潜酒加上汤及其余调味料炒匀上碟。

Ingredients:

180g deboned duck's web	60g green capsicum
2 cups water	90g baby corn
4 slices ginger	2 garlic cloves
2 shallots	2 tbsp oil
30g red chillies	

Marinade:

1 tbsp wine	1 tsp sugar
1 tbsp ginger juice	$^1/_4$ tsp pepper
1 tsp light soy	

Seasoning:

$^1/_4$ tsp salt	$^1/_4$ cup stock
1 tbsp hot broad bean paste	1 tsp light soy
	1 tsp sugar
1 tsp wine	1 tsp cornflour solution

Method:

◆ Mix the duck's web with the marinade and set aside for 30 minutes. Blanch in the boiling water with half the ginger and shallot for 10 minutes. Refresh and drain. Deseed the chillies and capsicum then cut into bite-sized pieces. Halve each baby corn. Mince the remaining ginger, shallot and garlic.

◆ Heat a wok and bring the oil to the boil. Sprinkle in the salt and saute the ginger, shallot and garlic until aromatic. Pour in the duck's webs and stir fry for 5 minutes. Mix in the broad bean paste, pepper and baby corn. Sizzle wine then stream in the stock and other seasoning. Toss thoroughly then dish.

银芽火鸭丝
PEKING DUCK MEAT WITH BEAN SPROUTS

材料：

银芽 250 克   蒜头 1 粒
烧鸭 150 克   油 2 汤匙
韭黄 15 克   姜丝 1/2 茶匙
葱 1 棵

调味：

酒 1 茶匙   糖 1 茶匙
生油 1 汤匙   麻油 1 茶匙

制法：

◆ 银芽摘妥洗净隔干水份。
◆ 烧鸭去骨切丝，韭黄及葱洗净切度，蒜头切片。
◆ 烧红锅加油 1 汤匙煮沸爆香蒜片，倒入银芽迅速炒数下盛起候用。
◆ 再烧热锅加入余油爆香姜丝及鸭丝，倾入银芽拌炒 10 秒钟。潲酒加入调味料，洒下韭黄及葱度兜匀，即可上碟。

Ingredients:

250g bean   1 spring onion
sprouts   1 garlic clove
150g roast duck   2 tbsp oil
15g white leeks   1/2 tsp shredded ginger

Seasoning:

1 tsp wine   1 tsp sugar
1 tbsp light soy   1 tsp sesame oil

Method:

◆ Trim, wash and drain the bean sprouts.
◆ Debone and shred the roast duck. Wash and section the white leeks and spring onion. Slice the garlic.
◆ Heat a wok until very hot and bring l tbsp of the oil to boil. Saute the garlic until aromatic then pour in the bean sprouts to stir briskly. Remove.
◆ Reheat the wak with the remaining oil to saute the shredded ginger and roast duck. Add the bean sprouts to stir fry for 10 seconds. Sizzle the wine, put in the seasoning then sprinkle in the white leeks and spring onion to mix thoroughly and dish.

鲍鱼火腿鸽汤

PIGEON HAM AND ABALONE SOUP

材料：

去皮鸽1只约1000克　　鲜鲍鱼500克
火腿60克　　　　　　　盐1汤匙
姜汁2汤匙　　　　　　　姜2片
酒1汤匙　　　　　　　　沸水8杯

调味：

盐1茶匙

制法：

◆ 将鸽洗净与火腿一同放于1/2锅水中，加姜汁、酒煮沸飞水。取出放水龙头下冲洗干净，火腿去尽肥肉后切片。

◆ 鲍鱼用盐擦匀后飞水清洗干净、姜片拍扁。

◆ 将鸽、火腿、鲍鱼及姜片同放在炖盅内，加入沸水，盖上盅盖，置深锅内加水1/2锅，以中火炖2小时。

◆ 揭盖调妥味即可上桌。

Ingredients:

1 skinned pigeon about　　500g abalones
1000g　　　　　　　　　　1 tbsp salt
60g Chinese ham　　　　　2 slices ginger
2 tbsp ginger juice　　　　8 cups boiling water
1 tbsp wine

Seasoning:

1 tsp salt

Method:

◆ Clean and blanch the pigeon with the ham in some boiling water. Add the ginger juice and wine to boil for 1 minute, refresh and drain. Slice the ham into thin pieces.

◆ Rub the abalone with the salt then blanch and refresh. Mash the ginger.

◆ Place the pigeon, ham, abalones and the ginger in an earthen pot. Pour in the water and cover with a lid. Sit the pot in a deep saucepan half filled with water. Bring to the boil and continue to simmer over moderate heat for 2 hours.

◆ Remove the lid and season to taste. Serve hot in the pot.

玫瑰醉鸽

PIGEON IN ROSE WINE

材料：

乳鸽 2 只   盐 2 汤匙
八角 3 粒   水 4 杯
桂皮 1 方英寸   玫瑰露 2 汤匙
姜 2 片

浸鸽料：

白卤水 1 杯   玫瑰露 $^1/_2$ 杯
上汤 $1^1/_2$ 杯   糖 1 汤匙

制法：

◆ 乳鸽用沸水洗净抹干。

◆ 八角、桂皮、姜、盐及水同放煲中煮 20 分钟后，将双鸽放入煮至重沸时，加入玫瑰露，熄火盖密焗 15 分钟，取出以水冲冻隔干。

◆ 浸鸽料混和调至合味。将双鸽开边放入浸过夜，即可斩件上碟。

Ingredients:

2 pigeons   3 tbsp salt
3 star anises   4 cups water
1 sq. in cinnamon bark   2 tbsp rose wine
2 slices ginger

Wine Sauce:

1 cup plain spicy sauce $^1/_2$ cup rose wine
$1^1/_2$ cups stock   1 tbsp sugar

Method:

◆ Bring a few cups of water to the boil and blanch the pigeons for 2 minutes. Clean and towel dry.

◆ Place the star anises, cinnamon bark, ginger, salt and water in a saucepan and bring it to the boil for 20 minutes. Put in the pigeons and reboil the sauce. Pour in the rose wine, turn off the heat and set aside for 15 minutes. Remove the pigeons, refresh and drain.

◆ Mix the sauce ingredients and adjust the flavour to taste. Half each pigeon then soak in the wine sauce and keep in the refrigerator overnight. Remove, chop into serving pieces and serve.

双火拌豆芽
SOYA BEAN SPROUTS WITH ROAST DUCK

材料：

大豆芽 300 克　　火鸭 60 克
油 1 汤匙　　　　火腿 60 克
葱头 2 粒　　　　姜 1 片

调味：

生抽 1 $^1/_2$ 汤匙　　胡椒粉 $^1/_4$ 茶匙
糖 1 汤匙　　　　麻油 1 茶匙

制法：

◆ 大豆芽摘去尾洗净以白锅略烙，再加油及葱头爆香。盛起晾凉候用。
◆ 火鸭及火腿皆切丝，姜洗净亦切丝。
◆ 将调味料放小碗中和匀淋在豆芽上拌妥，加入火鸭、火腿及姜丝再捞匀。盛在碟上。

Ingredients:

300g soya bean　　60g roast duck
sprouts　　　　　60g ham
1 tbsp oil　　　　1 slice ginger
2 shallots

Seasoning:

1$^1/_2$ tsp light soy　　$^1/_4$ tsp pepper
1 tbsp sugar　　　1 tsp sesame oil

Method:

◆ Trim, wash and parch the soya bean sprouts. Saute in a hot wok with the oil and shallots. Remove and leave to cool.
◆ Shred the roast duck and ham. Wash and shred the ginger.
◆ Mix the seasoning in a small bowl and pour over the bean sprouts. Add the shredded duck, ham and ginger to mix thoroughly. Dish and serve cold.

芋仔甋鴨

STEAMED DUCK WITH YAM

材料：

鴨 1 只重 2000 克	油 3 汤匙
姜汁 2 汤匙	芋仔 1000 克
酒 2 汤匙	鸭酱 1 杯
香盐 1 茶匙	姜茸 1 汤匙
老抽 2 汤匙	葱头茸 1 汤匙
蒜头茸 1 汤匙	

调味：

酒 1 汤匙	生抽 1 汤匙
水 1 杯	糖 1 汤匙

制法：

- ◆ 鴨洗净抹干，以姜汁、酒擦勻鴨身腌半小时。将香盐擦在鴨腹内。鴨皮扫上老抽候用。
- ◆ 烧红锅加 1 汤匙油煮沸，将鴨滑入煎至两面金黄色。
- ◆ 芋仔去皮洗净用另一汤匙油起锅，将 1/2 杯鸭酱与芋仔同爆透盛起候用。
- ◆ 用烧红锅放下余油 1 汤匙爆香姜、葱、蒜茸及其余鸭酱。将鴨滑入锅中滚满酱料。灒酒加水及调味同煮沸。铲出放在长碟上，将余下酱料涂入鴨肚内。转置蒸笼内蒸 1 小时。停火揭蒸笼盖，将芋仔排在鴨之四周，盖密再蒸半小时。
- ◆ 将鴨取出晾凉斩件，排在芋仔上。鴨汁重煮沸，淋在鴨件上即可上桌。

Ingredients:

1 duck, about 2000g	3 tbsp oil
2 tbsp ginger juice	1000g yam
2 tbsp wine	1 cup duck sauce
1 tsp spicy salt	1 tbsp minced ginger
2 tbsp dark soy	1 tbsp minced shallot
	1 tbsp minced garlic

Seasoning:

1 tbsp wine	1 tbsp light soy
1 cup water	1 tbsp sugar

Method:

- ◆ Rub the skin of the duck with the ginger juice and wine and marinate for 30 minutes. Spread the spicy salt inside the duck and coat the dark soy on the skin. Shallow fry the duck in 1 tbsp oil until golden brown.
- ◆ Shallow fry the yam in another tbsp oil, then add 1/2 cup of the duck sauce and saute thoroughly.
- ◆ Reheat the wok with the remaining oil and saute the ginger, shallot and garlic with the remaining duck sauce. Return the duck to the wok and coat with the sauce. Sizzle the wine, add the water and seasoning and bring to the boil. Remove the duck on to a platter and fill the stomach of the duck with the sauce. Arrange in the steamer and cook for 1 hour. Turn off the heat; add the yam, cover the steamer and leave on the hot stove for another 30 minutes.
- ◆ Chop the duck into serving pieces and put on top of the yam. Reboil the sauce and serve it with the duck.

圣诞酿鹅
STUFFED CHRISTMAS GOOSE

材料：

鹅 1 只 3000 克

鹅馅：

栗子 500 克	洋葱粒 1 杯
免治牛肉 250 克	西芹粒 1 杯
免治猪肉 250 克	烟肉 180 克切碎
油 2 汤匙	面粉 1/2 杯
水 1/2 杯	

调味：

盐 3 茶匙	鸡粉 1 茶匙
糖 1 汤匙	

涂皮料：

姜汁 2 汤匙	喼汁 2 汤匙
白酒 2 汤匙	

汁料：

水 4 杯	红萝卜片 60 克
鹅杂掌翼及部分骨	盐 1/2 茶匙
西芹 60 克	黄汁 1/2 杯（后加）

制法：

◆ 将鹅由背中间削开，取出内脏退去骨头，只留四柱骨（四肢）。鹅杂、掌翼及骨留作煮汁用。

◆ 栗子去衣煮熟挟烂成茸，免治牛肉及猪肉放大碗中加入一半调味腌 20 分钟。

◆ 烧红锅加油爆香洋葱及西芹，倾入栗子茸炒匀后盛起。

◆ 原锅将烟肉粒、免治牛及猪肉拌入炒匀。继将洋葱、西芹、栗子茸倒回锅中拌炒。面粉水及其余调味料开成浓浆流入捞匀调至合味，停火晾凉。

◆ 将已晾凉之鹅馅酿入鹅皮内至八分满，用幼白绳将鹅背缝好。

◆ 鹅皮外以涂皮料抹匀，吹干。放在已涂油烧热之焗盘架上，以 150℃焗半小时至金黄色。每半小时反身一次扫油。大约焗 2 小时即可取出。切片上碟以番茄、青瓜片、芫荽伴碟边。

汁料：

◆ 深锅 1 个加水将汁料放入，以慢火熬 1 小时。隔去渣滓加黄汁拌匀跟上。

Ingredient:

1 goose about 3000g

Stuffing:

500g chestnuts	1 cup diced celery
250g minced beef	180g diced bacon
250g minced pork	1/2 cup flour +
2 tbsp oil	1/2 cup water
1 cup diced onions	

Seasoning :

3 tsp salt	1 tsp chicken powder
1 tbsp sugar	

Coating Sauce:

2 tbsp ginger juice	2 tbsp Worcestershire
2 tbsp white wine	Sauce

Gravy:

4 cups water	60g sliced celery
giblets, wings and legs	60g sliced carrot
of the goose	1/2 tsp salt
250g goose bones	1/2 cup brown sauce

Method:

◆ Clean and debone the goose. Remove and retain the giblets, wings, legs and the bones for the gravy.

◆ Shell, cook and puree the chestnuts. Marinate the beef and pork with half of the seasoning for 20 minutes.

◆ Bring the oil to the boil in a wok to saute the onion and celery. Pour in the chestnut puree to stir fry thoroughly and remove.

◆ Reheat the wok and saute the diced bacon then add the minced beef and pork and stir fry for 2 minutes. Return the onion, celery and chestnut mix into the wok to fry evenly. Mix the flour, water and the remaining seasoning together into a batter and stream into the wok and simmer for 1 minute. Adjust the flavour to taste and set aside to cool.

◆ Fill the goose skin with the cooked stuffing until it is 3/4 full. Sew the opening with thread.

◆ Brush the goose skin with the coating sauce then hang up to dry. Put the goose on to a greased hot baking tray and bake in a 150℃ oven until golden. Turn every 30 minutes and baste with the dripping . Cook for 2 hours. Slice and arrange on a dish. Garnish with sliced tomatoes, cucumber and parsley if desired.

Gravy:

◆ Bring the water to the boil in a saucepan with all the sauce ingredients except the brown sauce. Simmer for 1 hour over low heat. Filter the sauce through a sieve, blend in the brown sauce and serve separately.

佳肴菜谱系列

家禽美食

欧阳纫溆编著

*

统　　版：潘晖文　宋文华

美术设计：刘嘉俊

广东旅游出版社出版发行

（广州市中山一路 30 号之一邮编：510600）

广州金羊彩印有限公司

厂址：广州市天河区高新技术开发区建中路 46 号

1808×2100 毫米　24 开　50 印张　72 千字

2000 年 3 月第一版 2000 年 3 月第一次印刷

印数：1—3000 册

书号：ISBN 7-80653-083-5/TS.01

定价全套：280.00 元（每册：28.00 元）